1969

This book may be kept

Sister Beatrice

Jerry & Barb
December, 1968

MOMENTS OF TRUTH

MOMENTS OF TRUTH

Edited by

Dan Herr and Joel Wells

DOUBLEDAY & COMPANY, INC.

GARDEN CITY, NEW YORK

Library of Congress Catalog Card Number 66-24327
Copyright © 1966 by Dan Herr and Joel Wells
All Rights Reserved
Printed in the United States of America

ACKNOWLEDGMENTS

Grateful acknowledgment is made to the following for the use of copyrighted material:

THE DEVIN-ADAIR CO. "Teresa" is from the short story collection *The Man Who Invented Sin and Other Stories* by Sean O'Faolain. Published and copyrighted 1948 by The Devin-Adair Co., New York. Reprinted by permission.

DOUBLEDAY & COMPANY, INC. Chapter 10 from *No Little Thing* by Elizabeth Ann Cooper. Copyright © 1960 by Elizabeth Ann Cooper; "Stories on the Verandah" from *The Saucer of Larks* by Brian Friel. Copyright © 1962 by Brian Friel; "The Trouble" from *Prince of Darkness and Other Stories* by J. F. Powers. Copyright 1944 by J. F. Powers. All reprinted by permission.

FARRAR, STRAUS & GIROUX, INC. "Revelation" from *Everything That Rises Must Converge* by Flannery O'Connor. Copyright © 1964 by the Estate of Mary Flannery O'Connor. Reprinted by permission.

HARCOURT, BRACE & WORLD, INC. "The Jilting of Granny Weatherall" from *Flowering Judas and Other Stories* by Katherine Anne Porter. Copyright © 1930, 1935, 1958, 1963 by Katherine Anne Porter. Reprinted by permission.

DAVID HIGHAM ASSOCIATES, LTD. Excerpt from *The Outsider* by Phyllis Bottome. Copyright © 1963 by The Atlantic Monthly Company, Boston, Mass. Reprinted by permission.

ALFRED A. KNOPF, INC. "The Face of Evil," from *More Stories by Frank O'Connor*. Copyright 1954 by Frank O'Connor. Originally appeared in *The New Yorker*. Reprinted by permission of Alfred A. Knopf, Inc. and A. D. Peters & Co.

WILLIAM MORROW & CO. "Prognosis" from *The Devil's Advocate* by Morris L. West. Copyright © 1959 by Morris L. West. Reprinted by permission.

HAROLD OBER ASSOCIATES "I, Said the Sparrow" by Arthur Roth in the December 1964–January 1965 issue of *The Critic*. Copyright © 1964 by Arthur Roth. Reprinted by permission.

RANDOM HOUSE, INC. "The Confrontation" from *Under the Sun of Satan* by Georges Bernanos. Copyright 1949 by Pantheon Books, Inc.; "The Trial of St. Thomas More" from *A Man for All Seasons* by Robert Bolt. Copyright © 1962 by Robert Bolt; "God Sees the Truth but Waits" by Leo Tolstoy, reprinted from *Best Russian Short Stories* edited by Thomas Seltzer. All reprinted by permission.

VIRGINIA RICE "The Devil in the Desert" by Paul Horgan. Copyright © 1950 by The Curtis Publishing Company. Reprinted by permission.

6 ACKNOWLEDGMENTS

THE SOCIETY OF AUTHORS Excerpt from Scene VI of *Saint Joan* by George Bernard Shaw. Reprinted by permission of The Public Trustee and The Society of Authors.

THE VIKING PRESS, INC. Excerpt from *The Power and the Glory* by Graham Greene. Copyright 1940 by Graham Greene. Reprinted by permission of The Viking Press, Inc. and Laurence Pollinger Limited.

CONTENTS

INTRODUCTION

While we readily admit that in choosing *Moments of Truth* as a title for this collection we risk being caught in the act of fraternizing with one of the more notorious clichés at large in the world today, it seemed to be, in spite of the risk, the best available label. "Moments of Crisis" might have done, for almost all of these short stories and excerpts do focus on a human crisis of one sort or another. But whether the crisis itself takes a physical, emotional, religious or psychological form, in this book the crisis is only the means or the occasion of getting at the truth—the doorway to an instant of understanding of a particular sort and of a particularly intense degree.

It is not always the fictional protagonist who is granted the benefit of this instant. As often as not it is the reader who profits. In one sense, of course, fiction itself, particularly the short story, can be defined as a moment of truth. But for this book we were looking for fiction which turned on that most elusive and most profound sort of truth—that which resides in man's relation to man and, sometimes, his relationship with God; fiction which fills the prescription contained in Congreve's phrase: "Eternity was in that moment."

But, we hasten to add, this is not meant to be an "inspirational" book, and certainly not a pious one—which will become immediately apparent to the reader. It is largely a serious book and, we hope, a provocative one. If it is guilty of any therapeutic intent, it is only to serve as a sort of literary antidote to all moderns who may find themselves still doubting the wisdom which lurks in Pascal's words: "We know the truth, not only by reason but by the heart."

DAN HERR
JOEL WELLS

MOMENTS OF TRUTH

REVELATION

Flannery O'Connor

The doctor's waiting room, which was very small, was almost
full when the Turpins entered and Mrs. Turpin, who was very
large, made it look even smaller by her presence. She stood
looming at the head of the magazine table set in the center of
it, a living demonstration that the room was inadequate and
ridiculous. Her little bright black eyes took in all the patients
as she sized up the seating situation. There was one vacant
chair and a place on the sofa occupied by a blond child in a
dirty blue romper who should have been told to move over
and make room for the lady. He was five or six, but Mrs.
Turpin saw at once that no one was going to tell him to move
over. He was slumped down in the seat, his arms idle at his sides
and his eyes idle in his head; his nose ran unchecked.

Mrs. Turpin put a firm hand on Claud's shoulder and said
in a voice that included anyone who wanted to listen, "Claud,
you sit in that chair there," and gave him a push down into
the vacant one. Claud was florid and bald and sturdy, somewhat shorter than Mrs. Turpin, but he sat down as if he were
accustomed to doing what she told him to.

Mrs. Turpin remained standing. The only man in the room
besides Claud was a lean stringy old fellow with a rusty hand
spread out on each knee, whose eyes were closed as if he were
asleep or dead or pretending to be so as not to get up and
offer her his seat. Her gaze settled agreeably on a well-dressed
grey-haired lady whose eyes met hers and whose expression
said: if that child belonged to me, he would have some manners
and move over—there's plenty of room there for you and him
too.

Claud looked up with a sigh and made as if to rise.

"Sit down," Mrs. Turpin said. "You know you're not supposed to stand on that leg. He has an ulcer on his leg," she explained.

Claud lifted his foot onto the magazine table and rolled his trouser leg up to reveal a purple swelling on a plump marble-white calf.

"My!" the pleasant lady said. "How did you do that?"

"A cow kicked him," Mrs. Turpin said.

"Goodness!" said the lady.

Claud rolled his trouser leg down.

"Maybe the little boy would move over," the lady suggested, but the child did not stir.

"Somebody will be leaving in a minute," Mrs. Turpin said. She could not understand why a doctor—with as much money as they made charging five dollars a day to just stick their head in the hospital door and look at you—couldn't afford a decent-sized waiting room. This one was hardly bigger than a garage. The table was cluttered with limp-looking magazines and at one end of it there was a big green glass ash tray full of cigaret butts and cotton wads with little blood spots on them. If she had had anything to do with the running of the place, that would have been emptied every so often. There were no chairs against the wall at the head of the room. It had a rectangular-shaped panel in it that permitted a view of the office where the nurse came and went and the secretary listened to the radio. A plastic fern in a gold pot sat in the opening and trailed its fronds down almost to the floor. The radio was softly playing gospel music.

Just then the inner door opened and a nurse with the highest stack of yellow hair Mrs. Turpin had ever seen put her face in the crack and called for the next patient. The woman sitting beside Claud grasped the two arms of her chair and hoisted herself up; she pulled her dress free from her legs and lumbered through the door where the nurse had disappeared.

Mrs. Turpin eased into the vacant chair, which held her

tight as a corset. "I wish I could reduce," she said, and rolled her eyes and gave a comic sigh.

"Oh, *you* aren't fat," the stylish lady said.

"Ooooo I am too," Mrs. Turpin said. "Claud he eats all he wants to and never weighs over one hundred and seventy-five pounds, but me I just look at something good to eat and I gain some weight," and her stomach and shoulders shook with laughter. "You can eat all you want to, can't you, Claud?" she asked, turning to him.

Claud only grinned.

"Well, as long as you have such a good disposition," the stylish lady said, "I don't think it makes a bit of difference what size you are. You just can't beat a good disposition."

Next to her was a fat girl of eighteen or nineteen, scowling into a thick blue book which Mrs. Turpin saw was entitled *Human Development.* The girl raised her head and directed her scowl at Mrs. Turpin as if she did not like her looks. She appeared annoyed that anyone should speak while she tried to read. The poor girl's face was blue with acne and Mrs. Turpin thought how pitiful it was to have a face like that at that age. She gave the girl a friendly smile but the girl only scowled the harder. Mrs. Turpin herself was fat but she had always had good skin, and, though she was forty-seven years old, there was not a wrinkle in her face except around her eyes from laughing too much.

Next to the ugly girl was the child, still in exactly the same position, and next to him was a thin leathery old woman in a cotton print dress. She and Claud had three sacks of chicken feed in their pump house that was in the same print. She had seen from the first that the child belonged with the old woman. She could tell by the way they sat—kind of vacant and white-trashy, as if they would sit there until Doomsday if nobody called and told them to get up. And at right angles but next to the well-dressed pleasant lady was a lank-faced woman who was certainly the child's mother. She had on a yellow sweat shirt and wine-colored slacks, both gritty-looking, and the rims of her lips were stained with snuff. Her dirty yellow hair was tied behind with a little piece of red paper ribbon. Worse than niggers any day, Mrs. Turpin thought.

The gospel hymn playing was, "When I looked up and He looked down," and Mrs. Turpin, who knew it, supplied the last line mentally, "And wona these days I know I'll we-eara Crown."

Without appearing to, Mrs. Turpin always noticed people's feet. The well-dressed lady had on red and grey suede shoes to match her dress. Mrs. Turpin had on her good black patent leather pumps. The ugly girl had on Girl Scout shoes and heavy socks. The old woman had on tennis shoes and the white-trashy mother had on what appeared to be bedroom slippers, black straw with gold braid threaded through them— exactly what you would have expected her to have on.

Sometimes at night when she couldn't go to sleep, Mrs. Turpin would occupy herself with the question of who she would have chosen to be if she couldn't have been herself. If Jesus had said to her before he made her, "There's only two places available for you. You can either be a nigger or white-trash," what would she have said? "Please, Jesus, please," she would have said, "just let me wait until there's another place available," and he would have said, "No, you have to go right now and I have only those two places so make up your mind." She would have wiggled and squirmed and begged and pleaded but it would have been no use and finally she would have said, "All right, make me a nigger then—but that don't mean a trashy one." And he would have made her a neat clean re-spectable Negro woman, herself but black.

Next to the child's mother was a red-headed youngish woman, reading one of the magazines and working a piece of chewing gum, hell for leather, as Claud would say. Mrs. Turpin could see the woman's feet. She was not white-trash, just common. Sometimes Mrs. Turpin occupied herself at night naming the classes of people. On the bottom of the heap were most colored people, not the kind she would have been if she had been one, but most of them; then next to them—not above, just away from—were the white-trash; then above them were the home-owners, and above them the home-and-land owners, to which she and Claud belonged. Above she and Claud were people with a lot of money and much bigger houses and much more land. But here the complexity of it would begin to bear in on her, for some of the people with a lot of money were common and ought to be below she and Claud and some of the people who had good blood had lost their money and had to rent and then there were colored people who owned their homes and land as well. There was a colored dentist in town who had two red Lincolns and a swimming pool and a farm with registered white-face cattle on it. Usually by the time she had fallen asleep all the classes of people were moiling and roiling around in her head, and she would dream they were all crammed in together in a box car, being ridden off to be put in a gas oven.

"That's a beautiful clock," she said and nodded to her right. It was a big wall clock, the face encased in a brass sunburst.

"Yes, it's very pretty," the stylish lady said agreeably. "And right on the dot too," she added, glancing at her watch.

The ugly girl beside her cast an eye upward at the clock, smirked, then looked directly at Mrs. Turpin and smirked again. Then she returned her eyes to her book. She was obviously the lady's daughter because, although they didn't look anything alike as to disposition, they both had the same shape of face and the same blue eyes. On the lady they sparkled pleasantly but in the girl's seared face they appeared alternately to smolder and to blaze.

What if Jesus had said, "All right, you can be white-trash or a nigger or ugly"!

Mrs. Turpin felt an awful pity for the girl, though she thought it was one thing to be ugly and another to act ugly.

The woman with the snuff-stained lips turned around in her chair and looked up at the clock. Then she turned back and appeared to look a little to the side of Mrs. Turpin. There was a cast in one of her eyes. "You want to know wher you can get you one of them ther clocks?" she asked in a loud voice.

"No, I already have a nice clock," Mrs. Turpin said. Once somebody like her got a leg in the conversation, she would be all over it.

"You can get you one with green stamps," the woman said. "That's most likely wher he got hisn. Save you up enough, you can get you most anythang. I got me some joo'ry."

Ought to have got you a wash rag and some soap, Mrs. Turpin thought.

"I get contour sheets with mine," the pleasant lady said.

The daughter slammed her book shut. She looked straight in front of her, directly through Mrs. Turpin and on through the yellow curtain and the plate glass window which made the wall behind her. The girl's eyes seemed lit all of a sudden with a peculiar light, an unnatural light like night road signs give. Mrs. Turpin turned her head to see if there was anything going on outside that she should see, but she could not see anything. Figures passing cast only a pale shadow through the curtain. There was no reason the girl should single her out for her ugly looks.

"Miss Finley," the nurse said, cracking the door. The gum-chewing woman got up and passed in front of her and Claud and went into the office. She had on red high-heeled shoes.

Directly across the table, the ugly girl's eyes were fixed on Mrs. Turpin as if she had some very special reason for disliking her.

"This is wonderful weather, isn't it?" the girl's mother said.

"It's good weather for cotton if you can get the niggers to pick it," Mrs. Turpin said, "but niggers don't want to pick cotton any more. You can't get the white folks to pick it and now you can't get the niggers—because they got to be right up there with the white folks."

"They gonna *try* anyways," the white-trash woman said, leaning forward.

"Do you have one of those cotton-picking machines?" the pleasant lady asked.

"No," Mrs. Turpin said, "they leave half the cotton in the field. We don't have much cotton anyway. If you want to make it farming now, you have to have a little of everything. We got a couple of acres of cotton and a few hogs and chickens and just enough white-face that Claud can look after them himself."

"One thang I don't want," the white-trash woman said, wiping her mouth with the back of her hand. "Hogs. Nasty stinking things, a-gruntin and a-rootin all over the place."

Mrs. Turpin gave her the merest edge of her attention. "Our hogs are not dirty and they don't stink," she said. "They're cleaner than some children I've seen. Their feet never touch the ground. We have a pig parlor—that's where you raise them on concrete," she explained to the pleasant lady, "and Claud scoots them down with the hose every afternoon and washes off the floor." Cleaner by far than that child right there, she thought. Poor nasty little thing. He had not moved except to put the thumb of his dirty hand into his mouth.

The woman turned her face away from Mrs. Turpin. "I know I wouldn't scoot down no hog with no hose," she said to the wall.

You wouldn't have no hog to scoot down, Mrs. Turpin said to herself.

"A-gruntin and a-rootin and a-groanin," the woman muttered.

"We got a little of everything," Mrs. Turpin said to the pleasant lady. "It's no use in having more than you can handle yourself with help like it is. We found enough niggers to pick our cotton this year but Claud he has to go after them and take them home again in the evening. They can't walk that half a mile. No they can't. I tell you," she said and laughed merrily, "I sure am tired of buttering up niggers, but you got to love em if you want em to work for you. When they come in the morning, I run out and I say, 'Hi yawl this morning?'

and when Claud drives them off to the field I just wave to beat the band and they just wave back." And she waved her hand rapidly to illustrate.

"Like you read out of the same book," the lady said, showing she understood perfectly.

"Child, yes," Mrs. Turpin said. "And when they come in from the field, I run out with a bucket of icewater. That's the way it's going to be from now on," she said. "You may as well face it."

"One thang I know," the white-trash woman said. "Two thangs I ain't going to do: love no niggers or scoot down no hog with no hose." And she let out a bark of contempt.

The look that Mrs. Turpin and the pleasant lady exchanged indicated they both understood that you had to *have* certain things before you could *know* certain things. But every time Mrs. Turpin exchanged a look with the lady, she was aware that the ugly girl's peculiar eyes were still on her, and she had trouble bringing her attention back to the conversation.

"When you got something," she said, "you got to look after it." And when you ain't got a thing but breath and britches, she added to herself, you can afford to come to town every morning and just sit on the Court House coping and spit.

A grotesque revolving shadow passed across the curtain behind her and was thrown palely on the opposite wall. Then a bicycle clattered down against the outside of the building. The door opened and a colored boy glided in with a tray from the drug store. It had two large red and white paper cups on it with tops on them. He was a tall, very black boy in discolored white pants and a green nylon shirt. He was chewing gum slowly, as if to music. He set the tray down in the office opening next to the fern and stuck his head through to look for the secretary. She was not in there. He rested his arms on the ledge and waited, his narrow bottom stuck out, swaying slowly to the left and right. He raised a hand over his head and scratched the base of his skull.

"You see that button there, boy?" Mrs. Turpin said. "You

can punch that and she'll come. She's probably in the back somewhere."

"Is thas right?" the boy said agreeably, as if he had never seen the button before. He leaned to the right and put his finger on it. "She sometime out," he said and twisted around to face his audience, his elbows behind him on the counter. The nurse appeared and he twisted back again. She handed him a dollar and he rooted in his pocket and made the change and counted it out to her. She gave him fifteen cents for a tip and he went out with the empty tray. The heavy door swung to slowly and closed at length with the sound of suction. For a moment no one spoke.

"They ought to send all them niggers back to Africa," the white-trash woman said. "That's wher they come from in the first place."

"Oh, I couldn't do without my good colored friends," the pleasant lady said.

"There's a heap of things worse than a nigger," Mrs. Turpin agreed. "It's all kinds of them just like it's all kinds of us."

"Yes, and it takes all kinds to make the world go round," the lady said in her musical voice.

As she said it, the raw-complexioned girl snapped her teeth together. Her lower lip turned downwards and inside out, revealing the pale pink inside of her mouth. After a second it rolled back up. It was the ugliest face Mrs. Turpin had ever seen anyone make and for a moment she was certain that the girl had made it at her. She was looking at her as if she had known and disliked her all her life—all of Mrs. Turpin's life, it seemed too, not just all the girl's life. Why, girl, I don't even know you, Mrs. Turpin said silently.

She forced her attention back to the discussion. "It wouldn't be practical to send them back to Africa," she said. "They wouldn't want to go. They got it too good here."

"Wouldn't be what they wanted—if I had anythang to do with it," the woman said.

"It wouldn't be a way in the world you could get all the

niggers back over there," Mrs. Turpin said. "They'd be hiding out and lying down and turning sick on you and wailing and hollering and raring and pitching. It wouldn't be a way in the world to get them over there."

"They got over here," the trashy woman said. "Get back like they got over."

"It wasn't so many of them then," Mrs. Turpin explained.

The woman looked at Mrs. Turpin as if here was an idiot indeed but Mrs. Turpin was not bothered by the look, considering where it came from.

"Nooo," she said. "They're going to stay here where they can go to New York and marry white folks and improve their color. That's what they all want to do, every one of them, improve their color."

"You know what comes of that, don't you?" Claud asked.

"No, Claud, what?" Mrs. Turpin said.

Claud's eyes twinkled. "White-faced niggers," he said with never a smile.

Everybody in the office laughed except the white-trash and the ugly girl. The girl gripped the book in her lap with white fingers. The trashy woman looked around her from face to face as if she thought they were all idiots. The old woman in the feed sack dress continued to gaze expressionless across the floor at the high-top shoes of the man opposite her, the one who had been pretending to be asleep when the Turpins came in. He was laughing heartily, his hands still spread out on his knees. The child had fallen to the side and was lying now almost face down in the old woman's lap.

While they recovered from their laughter, the nasal chorus on the radio kept the room from silence.

> *"You go to blank blank*
> *And I'll go to mine*
> *But we'll all blank along*
> *To-geth-ther,*

And all along the blank
We'll hep each other out
Smile-ling in any kind of
Weath-ther!"

Mrs. Turpin didn't catch every word but she caught enough to agree with the spirit of the song and it turned her thoughts sober. To help anybody out that needed it was her philosophy of life. She never spared herself when she found somebody in need, whether they were white or black, trash or decent. And of all she had to be thankful for, she was most thankful that this was so. If Jesus had said, "You can be high society and have all the money you want and be thin and svelte-like, but you can't be a good woman with it," she would have had to say, "Well don't make me that then. Make me a good woman and it don't matter what else, how fat or how ugly or how poor!" Her heart rose. He had not made her a nigger or white-trash or ugly! He had made her herself and given her a little of everything. Jesus, thank you! she said. Thank you thank you thank you! Whenever she counted her blessings she felt as buoyant as if she weighed one hundred and twenty-five pounds instead of one hundred and eighty.

"What's wrong with your little boy?" the pleasant lady asked the white-trashy woman.

"He has a ulcer," the woman said proudly. "He ain't give me a minute's peace since he was born. Him and her are just alike," she said, nodding at the old woman, who was running her leathery fingers through the child's pale hair. "Look like I can't get nothing down them two but Co'Cola and candy."

That's all you try to get down em, Mrs. Turpin said to herself. Too lazy to light the fire. There was nothing you could tell her about people like them that she didn't know already. And it was not just that they didn't have anything. Because if you gave them everything, in two weeks it would all be broken or filthy or they would have chopped it up for light-wood. She knew all this from her own experience. Help them you must, but help them you couldn't.

All at once the ugly girl turned her lips inside out again. Her eyes were fixed like two drills on Mrs. Turpin. This time there was no mistaking that there was something urgent behind them.

Girl, Mrs. Turpin exclaimed silently, I haven't done a thing to you! The girl might be confusing her with somebody else. There was no need to sit by and let herself be intimidated. "You must be in college," she said boldly, looking directly at the girl. "I see you reading a book there."

The girl continued to stare and pointedly did not answer.

Her mother blushed at this rudeness. "The lady asked you a question, Mary Grace," she said under her breath.

"I have ears," Mary Grace said.

The poor mother blushed again. "Mary Grace goes to Wellesley College," she explained. She twisted one of the buttons on her dress. "In Massachusetts," she added with a grimace. "And in the summer she just keeps right on studying. Just reads all the time, a real book worm. She's done real well at Wellesley; she's taking English and Math and History and Psychology and Social Studies," she rattled on, "and I think it's too much. I think she ought to get out and have fun."

The girl looked as if she would like to hurl them all through the plate glass window.

"Way up north," Mrs. Turpin murmured and thought, well, it hasn't done much for her manners.

"I'd almost rather to have him sick," the white-trash woman said, wrenching the attention back to herself. "He's so mean when he ain't. Look like some children just take natural to meanness. It's some gets bad when they get sick but he was the opposite. Took sick and turned good. He don't give me no trouble now. It's me waitin to see the doctor," she said.

If I was going to send anybody back to Africa, Mrs. Turpin thought, it would be your kind, woman. "Yes, indeed," she said aloud, but looking up at the ceiling, "it's a heap of things worse than a nigger." And dirtier than a hog, she added to herself.

"I think people with bad dispositions are more to be pitied than anyone on earth," the pleasant lady said in a voice that was decidedly thin.

"I thank the Lord he has blessed me with a good one," Mrs. Turpin said. "The day has never dawned that I couldn't find something to laugh at."

"Not since she married me anyways," Claud said with a comical straight face.

Everybody laughed except the girl and the white-trash.

Mrs. Turpin's stomach shook. "He's such a caution," she said, "that I can't help but laugh at him."

The girl made a loud ugly noise through her teeth.

Her mother's mouth grew thin and tight. "I think the worst thing in the world," she said, "is an ungrateful person. To have everything and not appreciate it. I know a girl," she said, "who has parents who would give her anything, a little brother who loves her dearly, who is getting a good education, who wears the best clothes, but who can never say a kind word to anyone, who never smiles, who just criticizes and complains all day long."

"Is she too old to paddle?" Claud asked.

The girl's face was almost purple.

"Yes," the lady said, "I'm afraid there's nothing to do but leave her to her folly. Some day she'll wake up and it'll be too late."

"It never hurt anyone to smile," Mrs. Turpin said. "It just makes you feel better all over."

"Of course," the lady said sadly, "but there are just some people you can't tell anything to. They can't take criticism."

"If it's one thing I am," Mrs. Turpin said with feeling, "it's grateful. When I think who all I could have been besides myself and what all I got, a little of everything, and a good disposition besides, I just feel like shouting, 'Thank you, Jesus, for making everything the way it is!' It could have been different!" For one thing, somebody else could have got Claud. At the thought of this, she was flooded with gratitude and a terrible pang of joy ran through her. "Oh thank you, Jesus, Jesus, thank you!" she cried aloud.

The book struck her directly over her left eye. It struck almost at the same instant that she realized the girl was about to hurl it. Before she could utter a sound, the raw face came crashing across the table toward her, howling. The girl's fingers sank like clamps into the soft flesh of her neck. She heard the mother cry out and Claud shout, "Whoa!" There was an instant when she was certain that she was about to be in an earthquake.

All at once her vision narrowed and she saw everything as if it were happening in a small room far away, or as if she were looking at it through the wrong end of a telescope. Claud's face crumpled and fell out of sight. The nurse ran in, then out, then in again. Then the gangling figure of the doctor rushed out of the inner door. Magazines flew this way and that as the table turned over. The girl fell with a thud and Mrs. Turpin's vision suddenly reversed itself and she saw everything large instead of small. The eyes of the white-trashy woman were staring hugely at the floor. There the girl, held down on one side by the nurse and on the other by her mother, was wrenching and turning in their grasp. The doctor was kneeling astride her, trying to hold her arm down. He managed after a second to sink a long needle into it.

Mrs. Turpin felt entirely hollow except for her heart which swung from side to side as if it were agitated in a great empty drum of flesh.

"Somebody that's not busy call for the ambulance," the doctor said in the off-hand voice young doctors adopt for terrible occasions.

Mrs. Turpin could not have moved a finger. The old man who had been sitting next to her skipped nimbly into the office and made the call, for the secretary still seemed to be gone.

"Claud!" Mrs. Turpin called.

He was not in his chair. She knew she must jump up and find him but she felt like some one trying to catch a train in a dream, when everything moves in slow motion and the faster you try to run the slower you go.

"Here I am," a suffocated voice, very unlike Claud's, said.

He was doubled up in the corner on the floor, pale as paper, holding his leg. She wanted to get up and go to him but she could not move. Instead, her gaze was drawn slowly downward to the churning face on the floor, which she could see over the doctor's shoulder.

The girl's eyes stopped rolling and focused on her. They seemed a much lighter blue than before, as if a door that had been tightly closed behind them was now open to admit light and air.

Mrs. Turpin's head cleared and her power of motion returned. She leaned forward until she was looking directly into the fierce brilliant eyes. There was no doubt in her mind that the girl did know her, knew her in some intense and personal way, beyond time and place and condition. "What you got to say to me?" she asked hoarsely and held her breath, waiting, as for a revelation.

The girl raised her head. Her gaze locked with Mrs. Turpin's. "Go back to hell where you came from, you old wart hog," she whispered. Her voice was low but clear. Her eyes burned for a moment as if she saw with pleasure that her message had struck its target.

Mrs. Turpin sank back in her chair.

After a moment the girl's eyes closed and she turned her head wearily to the side.

The doctor rose and handed the nurse the empty syringe. He leaned over and put both hands for a moment on the mother's shoulders, which were shaking. She was sitting on the floor, her lips pressed together, holding Mary Grace's hand in her lap. The girl's fingers were gripped like a baby's around her thumb. "Go on to the hospital," he said. "I'll call and make the arrangements.

"Now let's see that neck," he said in a jovial voice to Mrs. Turpin. He began to inspect her neck with his first two fingers. Two little moon-shaped lines like pink fish bones were indented over her windpipe. There was the beginning of an angry red swelling above her eye. His fingers passed over this also.

"Lea' me be," she said thickly and shook him off. "See about Claud. She kicked him."

"I'll see about him in a minute," he said and felt her pulse. He was a thin grey-haired man, given to pleasantries. "Go home and have yourself a vacation the rest of the day," he said and patted her on the shoulder.

Quit your pattin me, Mrs. Turpin growled to herself.

"And put an ice pack over that eye," he said. Then he went and squatted down beside Claud and looked at his leg. After a moment he pulled him up and Claud limped after him into the office.

Until the ambulance came, the only sounds in the room were the tremulous moans of the girl's mother, who continued to sit on the floor. The white-trash woman did not take her eyes off the girl. Mrs. Turpin looked straight ahead at nothing. Presently the ambulance drew up, a long dark shadow, behind the curtain. The attendants came in and set the stretcher down beside the girl and lifted her expertly onto it and carried her out. The nurse helped the mother gather up her things. The shadow of the ambulance moved silently away and the nurse came back in the office.

"That ther girl is going to be a lunatic, ain't she?" the white-trash woman asked the nurse, but the nurse kept on to the back and never answered her.

"Yes, she's going to be a lunatic," the white-trash woman said to the rest of them.

"Po' critter," the old woman murmured. The child's face was still in her lap. His eyes looked idly out over her knees. He had not moved during the disturbance except to draw one leg up under him.

"I thank Gawd," the white-trash woman said fervently, "I ain't a lunatic."

Claud came limping out and the Turpins went home.

As their pick-up truck turned into their own dirt road and made the crest of the hill, Mrs. Turpin gripped the window ledge and looked out suspiciously. The land sloped gracefully down through a field dotted with lavender weeds and at the start of the rise their small yellow frame house, with its little flower beds spread out around it like a fancy apron, sat primly in its accustomed place between two giant hickory trees. She would not have been startled to see a burnt wound between two blackened chimneys.

Neither of them felt like eating so they put on their house clothes and lowered the shade in the bedroom and lay down, Claud with his leg on a pillow and herself with a damp washcloth over her eye. The instant she was flat on her back, the image of a razor-backed hog with warts on its face and horns coming out behind its ears snorted into her head. She moaned, a low quiet moan.

"I am not," she said tearfully, "a wart hog. From hell." But the denial had no force. The girl's eyes and her words, even the tone of her voice, low but clear, directed only to her, brooked no repudiation. She had been singled out for the message, though there was trash in the room to whom it might justly have been applied. The full force of this fact struck her only now. There was a woman there who was neglecting her own child but she had been overlooked. The message had been given to Ruby Turpin, a respectable, hard-working, church-going woman. The tears dried. Her eyes began to burn instead with wrath.

She rose on her elbow and the washcloth fell into her hand. Claud was lying on his back, snoring. She wanted to tell him what the girl had said. At the same time, she did not wish to put the image of herself as a wart hog from hell into his mind.

"Hey, Claud," she muttered and pushed his shoulder.

Claud opened one pale baby blue eye.

She looked into it warily. He did not think about anything. He just went his way.

"Wha, whasit?" he said and closed the eye again.

"Nothing," she said. "Does your leg pain you?"

"Hurts like hell," Claud said.

"It'll quit terreckly," she said and lay back down. In a moment Claud was snoring again. For the rest of the afternoon they lay there. Claud slept. She scowled at the ceiling. Occasionally she raised her fist and made a small stabbing motion over her chest as if she was defending her innocence to invisible guests who were like the comforters of Job, reasonable-seeming but wrong.

About five-thirty Claud stirred. "Got to go after those niggers," he sighed, not moving.

She was looking straight up as if there were unintelligible handwriting on the ceiling. The protuberance over her eye had turned a greenish-blue. "Listen here," she said.

"What?"

"Kiss me."

Claud leaned over and kissed her loudly on the mouth. He pinched her side and their hands interlocked. Her expression of ferocious concentration did not change. Claud got up, groaning and growling, and limped off. She continued to study the ceiling.

She did not get up until she heard the pick-up truck coming back with the Negroes. Then she rose and thrust her feet in her brown oxfords, which she did not bother to lace, and stumped out onto the back porch and got her red plastic bucket. She emptied a tray of ice cubes into it and filled it half full of water and went out into the back yard. Every afternoon after Claud brought the hands in, one of the boys helped him put out hay and the rest waited in the back of the truck until he was ready to take them home. The truck was parked in the shade under one of the hickory trees.

"Hi yawl this evening?" Mrs. Turpin asked grimly, appearing with the bucket and the dipper. There were three women and a boy in the truck.

"Us doin nicely," the oldest woman said. "Hi you doin?" and her gaze stuck immediately on the dark lump on Mrs. Turpin's forehead. "You done fell down, ain't you?" she asked in a solicitous voice. The old woman was dark and almost toothless. She had on an old felt hat of Claud's set back on her head. The other two women were younger and lighter and they both had new bright green sun hats. One of them had hers on her head; the other had taken hers off and the boy was grinning beneath it.

Mrs. Turpin set the bucket down on the floor of the truck. "Yawl hep yourselves," she said. She looked around to make sure Claud had gone. "No. I didn't fall down," she said, folding her arms. "It was something worse than that."

"Ain't nothing bad happen to you!" the old woman said. She said it as if they all knew that Mrs. Turpin was protected in some special way by Divine Providence. "You just had you a little fall."

"We were in town at the doctor's office for where the cow kicked Mr. Turpin," Mrs. Turpin said in a flat tone that indicated they could leave off their foolishness. "And there was this girl there. A big fat girl with her face all broke out. I could look at that girl and tell she was peculiar but I couldn't tell how. And me and her mama were just talking and going along and all of a sudden WHAM! She throws this big book she was reading at me and . . ."

"Naw!" the old woman cried out.

"And then she jumps over the table and commences to choke me."

"Hi come she do that?" the old woman asked. "What ail her?"

Mrs. Turpin only glared in front of her.

"Somethin ail her," the old woman said.

"They carried her off in an ambulance," Mrs. Turpin continued, "but before she went she was rolling on the floor and they were trying to hold her down to give her a shot and she said something to me." She paused. "You know what she said to me?"

"What she say?" they asked.

"She said," Mrs. Turpin began, and stopped, her face very dark and heavy. The sun was getting whiter and whiter, blanching the sky overhead so that the leaves of the hickory tree were black in the face of it. She could not bring forth the words. "Something real ugly," she muttered.

"She sho shouldn't said nothin ugly to you," the old woman said. "You so sweet. You the sweetest lady I know."

"She pretty too," the one with the hat on said.

"And stout," the other one said. "I never knowed no sweeter white lady."

"That's the truth befo' Jesus," the old woman said. "Amen! You des as sweet and pretty as you can be."

Mrs. Turpin knew just exactly how much Negro flattery was worth and it added to her rage. "She said," she began again and finished this time with a fierce rush of breath, "that I was an old wart hog from hell."

There was an astounded silence.

"Where she at?" the youngest woman cried in a piercing voice.

"Lemme see her. I'll kill her!"

"I'll kill her with you!" the other one cried.

"She b'long in the sylum," the old woman said emphatically. "You the sweetest white lady I know."

"She pretty too," the other two said. "Stout as she can be and sweet. Jesus satisfied with her!"

"Deed he is," the old woman declared.

Idiots! Mrs. Turpin growled to herself. You could never say anything intelligent to a nigger. You could talk at them but not with them. "Yawl ain't drunk your water," she said shortly. "Leave the bucket in the truck when you're finished with it. I got more to do than just stand around and pass the time of day," and she moved off and into the house.

She stood for a moment in the middle of the kitchen. The dark protuberance over her eye looked like a miniature tornado cloud which might any moment sweep across the horizon of her brow. Her lower lip protruded dangerously. She squared her massive shoulders. Then she marched into the front of the house and out the side door and started down the road to the pig parlor. She had the look of a woman going single-handed, weaponless, into battle.

The sun was a deep yellow now like a harvest moon and was riding westward very fast over the far tree line as if it meant to reach the hogs before she did. The road was rutted and she kicked several good-sized stones out of her path as she strode along. The pig parlor was on a little knoll at the end of a lane that ran off from the side of the barn. It was a square of concrete as large as a small room, with a board fence about four feet high around it. The concrete floor sloped slightly so that the hog wash could drain off into a trench where it was carried to the field for fertilizer. Claud was standing on the outside, on the edge of the concrete, hanging onto the top board, hosing down the floor inside. The hose was connected to the faucet of a water trough nearby.

Mrs. Turpin climbed up beside him and glowered down at the hogs inside. There were seven long-snouted bristly shoats in it—tan with liver-colored spots—and an old sow a few weeks off from farrowing. She was lying on her side grunting. The shoats were running about shaking themselves like idiot children, their little slit pig eyes searching the floor for anything left. She had read that pigs were the most intelligent animal. She doubted it. They were supposed to be smarter than dogs. There had even been a pig astronaut. He had performed his assignment perfectly but died of a heart attack afterwards because they left him in his electric suit, sitting upright throughout his examination when naturally a hog should be on all fours.

A-gruntin and a-rootin and a-groanin.

"Gimme that hose," she said, yanking it away from Claud. "Go on and carry them niggers home and then get off that leg."

"You look like you might have swallowed a mad dog," Claud observed, but he got down and limped off. He paid no attention to her humors.

Until he was out of earshot, Mrs. Turpin stood on the side of the pen, holding the hose and pointing the stream of water at the hind quarters of any shoat that looked as if it might try to lie down. When he had had time to get over the hill, she turned her head slightly and her wrathful eyes scanned the path. He was nowhere in sight. She turned back again and seemed to gather herself up. Her shoulders rose and she drew in her breath.

"What do you send me a message like that for?" she said in a low fierce voice, barely above a whisper but with the force of a shout in its concentrated fury. "How am I a hog and me both? How am I saved and from hell too?" Her free fist was knotted and with the other she gripped the hose, blindly pointing the stream of water in and out of the eye of the old sow whose outraged squeal she did not hear.

The pig parlor commanded a view of the back pasture where their twenty beef cows were gathered around the hay-bales Claud and the boy had put out. The freshly cut pasture sloped down to the highway. Across it was their cotton field and beyond that a dark green dusty wood which they owned as well. The sun was behind the wood, very red, looking over the paling of trees like a farmer inspecting his own hogs.

"Why me?" she rumbled. "It's no trash around here, black or white, that I haven't given to. And break my back to the bone every day working. And do for the church."

She appeared to be the right size woman to command the arena before her. "How am I a hog?" she demanded. "Exactly how am I like them?" and she jabbed the stream of water at the shoats. "There was plenty of trash there. It didn't have to be me.

"If you like trash better, go get yourself some trash then," she railed. "You could have made me trash. Or a nigger. If trash is what you wanted why didn't you make me trash?" She shook her fist with the hose in it and a watery snake appeared momentarily in the air. "I could quit working and take it easy and be filthy," she growled. "Lounge about the sidewalks all day drinking root beer. Dip snuff and spit in every puddle and have it all over my face. I could be nasty.

"Or you could have made me a nigger. It's too late for me to be a nigger," she said with deep sarcasm, "but I could act like one. Lay down in the middle of the road and stop traffic. Roll on the ground."

In the deepening light everything was taking on a mysterious hue. The pasture was growing a peculiar glassy green and the streak of highway had turned lavender. She braced herself for a final assault and this time her voice rolled out over the pasture. "Go on," she yelled, "call me a hog! Call me a hog again. From hell. Call me a wart hog from hell. Put that bottom rail on top. There'll still be a top and bottom!"

A garbled echo returned to her.

A final surge of fury shook her and she roared, "Who do you think you are?"

The color of everything, field and crimson sky, burned for a moment with a transparent intensity. The question carried over the pasture and across the highway and the cotton field and returned to her clearly like an answer from beyond the wood.

She opened her mouth but no sound came out of it.

A tiny truck, Claud's appeared on the highway, heading rapidly out of sight. Its gears scraped thinly. It looked like a child's toy. At any moment a bigger truck might smash into it and scatter Claud's and the niggers' brains all over the road.

Mrs. Turpin stood there, her gaze fixed on the highway, all

her muscles rigid, until in five or six minutes the truck re-
appeared, returning. She waited until it had had time to turn
into their own road. Then like a monumental statue coming to
life, she bent her head slowly and gazed, as if through the
very heart of mystery, down into the pig parlor at the hogs.
They had settled all in one corner around the old sow who was
grunting softly. A red glow suffused them. They appeared to
pant with a secret life.

Until the sun slipped finally behind the tree line, Mrs.
Turpin remained there with her gaze bent to them as if she
were absorbing some abysmal life-giving knowledge. At last she
lifted her head. There was only a purple streak in the sky,
cutting through a field of crimson and leading, like an ex-
tension of the highway, into the descending dusk. She raised
her hands from the side of the pen in a gesture hieratic and
profound. A visionary light settled in her eyes. She saw the
streak as a vast swinging bridge extending upward from the
earth through a field of living fire. Upon it a vast horde of
souls were rumbling toward heaven. There were whole com-
panies of white-trash, clean for the first time in their lives, and
bands of black niggers in white robes, and battalions of freaks
and lunatics shouting and clapping and leaping like frogs. And
bringing up the end of the procession was a tribe of people whom
she recognized at once as those who, like herself and Claud,
had always had a little of everything and the God-given wit to
use it right. She leaned forward to observe them closer. They
were marching behind the others with great dignity, account-
able as they had always been for good order and common
sense and respectable behavior. They alone were on key. Yet
she could see by their shocked and altered faces that even
their virtues were being burned away. She lowered her hands
and gripped the rail of the hog pen, her eyes small but fixed
unblinkingly on what lay ahead. In a moment the vision faded
but she remained where she was, immobile.

At length she got down and turned off the faucet and made

her slow way on the darkening path to the house. In the woods around her the invisible cricket choruses had struck up, but what she heard were the voices of the souls climbing upward into the starry field and shouting hallelujah.

PROGNOSIS

Morris L. West

It was his profession to prepare other men for death; it shocked him to be so unready for his own.

He was a reasonable man and reason told him that a man's death sentence is written on his palm the day he is born; he was a cold man, little troubled by passion, irked not at all by discipline, yet his first impulse had been a wild clinging to the illusion of immortality.

It was part of the decency of Death that he should come unheralded with face covered and hands concealed, at the hour when he was least expected. He should come slowly, softly, like his brother Sleep—or swiftly and violently like the consummation of the act of love, so that the moment of surrender would be a stillness and satiety instead of wrenching separation of spirit and flesh.

The decency of Death. It was the thing men hoped for vaguely, prayed for if they were disposed to pray, regretted bitterly when they knew it would be denied to them. Blaise Meredith was regretting it now, as he sat in the thin spring sunshine, watching the slow, processional swans on the Serpentine, the courting couples on the grass, the leashed poodles trotting fastidiously along the paths at the flirting skirts of their owners.

In the midst of all this life—the thrusting grass, the trees bursting with new sap, the nodding of crocus and daffodil, the languid love-play of youth, the vigor of the elderly strollers—he alone, it seemed, had been marked to die. There was no mistaking the urgency or the finality of the mandate. It was written, for all to read, not in the lines of his palm, but in the square sheet of photographic negative where a small gray blur spelt out his sentence.

"Carcinoma!" The blunt finger of the surgeon had lingered a moment on the center of the gray blur, then moved outward tracing the diffusion of the tumor. "Slow-growing but well established. I've seen too many to be mistaken in this one."

As he watched the small translucent screen, and the spatulate finger moving across it, Blaise Meredith had been struck by the irony of the situation. All his life had been spent confronting others with the truth about themselves, the guilts that harried them, the lusts that debased them, the follies that diminished them. Now he was looking into his own guts where a small malignancy was growing like a mandrake root towards the day when it would destroy him.

He asked calmly enough:

"Is it operable?"

The surgeon switched off the light behind the viewing screen so that the small gray death faded into opacity; then he sat down, adjusting the desk lamp so that his own face was in shadow and that of his patient was lit like a marble head in a museum.

Blaise Meredith noted the small contrivance and understood it. They were both professionals. Each in his own calling dealt with human animals. Each must preserve a clinical detachment, lest he spend too much of himself and be left as weak and fearful as his patients.

The surgeon leaned back in his chair, picked up a paper-knife and held it poised as delicately as a scalpel. He waited a moment, gathering the words, choosing this one, discarding that, then laying them down in a pattern of meticulous accuracy.

"I can operate, yes. If I do, you'll be dead in three months."

"If you don't?"

"You'll live a little longer and die a little more painfully."

"How much longer?"

"Six months. Twelve at the outside."

"It's a grim choice."

"You must make it for yourself."

"I understand that."

The surgeon relaxed in his chair. The worst was over now. He had not been mistaken in his man. He was intelligent, ascetic, self-contained. He would survive the shock and accommodate himself to the inevitable. When the agony began he would wear it with a certain dignity. His Church would guarantee him against want and bury him with honor when he died; and, if there were none to mourn him, this too might be counted the final reward for celibacy, to slip out of life without regret for its pleasures or fear of its unfulfilled obligations.

Blaise Meredith's calm, dry voice cut across his thought:

"I'll think about what you've told me. In case I should decide not to have an operation—go back to my work—would you be good enough to write me a report to my local doctor? A full prognosis, a prescription, perhaps?"

"With pleasure, Monsignor Meredith. You work in Rome, I believe? Unfortunately I don't write Italian."

Blaise Meredith permitted himself a small wintry smile.

"I'll translate it myself. It should make an interesting exercise."

"I admire your courage, Monsignor. I don't subscribe to the Roman faith, or to any faith for that matter, but I imagine you find it a great consolation at a time like this."

"I hope I may, Doctor," said Blaise Meredith, simply, "but I've been a priest too long to expect it."

Now he was sitting on a park bench in the sun, with the air full of spring and the future a brief, empty prospect spilling over into eternity. Once, in his student days, he had heard an old missioner preach on the raising of Lazarus from the dead: how Christ had stood before the sealed vault and ordered it opened, so that the smell of corruption issued on the still, dry air of summer; how Lazarus at the summons had come out, stumbling in the cerecloths, to stand blinking in the sun. What had he felt at that moment? the old man asked. What price had he paid for this return to the world of the living? Did he go maimed ever afterwards so that every rose smelled of decay and every golden girl was a shambling skeleton? Or did he walk in a dazzle of wonder at the newness of things, his heart tender with pity and love for the human family?

The speculation had interested Meredith for years. Once he had toyed with the idea of writing a novel about it. Now, at last, he had the answer. Nothing was so sweet to man as life; nothing was more precious than time; nothing more reassuring than the touch of earth and grass, the whisper of moving air, the smell of new blossoms, the sound of voices and traffic and high birdsongs.

This was the thing that troubled him. He had been twenty years a priest, vowed to the affirmation that life was a transient imperfection, the earth a pale symbol of its maker, the soul an immortal in mortal clay beating itself wary for release into the ambient arms of the Almighty. Now that his own release was promised, the date of deliverance set, why could he not accept it—if not with joy, at least with confidence?

What did he cling to that he had not long since rejected? A woman? A child? A family? There was no one living who belonged to him. Possessions? They were few enough—a small apartment near the Porta Angelica, a few ornaments, a roomful of books, a modest stipend from the Congregation of Rites, an annuity left to him by his mother. Nothing there to tempt a man back from the threshold of the great revelation. Career? Something in that maybe—Auditor to the Sacred Congregation of Rites, personal assistant to the Prefect himself, Eugenio Cardinal Marotta. It was a position of influence, of flattering confidence. One sat in the shadow of the Pontiff. One watched the intricate subtle workings of a great theocracy. One lived in simple comfort. One had time to study, liberty to act freely within the limits of policy and discretion. Something in that . . . but not enough—not half enough for a man who hungered for the Perfect Union which he preached.

Perhaps that was the core of it. He had never been hungry

for anything. He had always had everything he wanted, and he had never wanted more than was available to him. He had accepted the discipline of the Church and the Church had given him security, comfort and scope for his talents. More than most men he had achieved contentment—and if he had never asked for happiness it was because he had never been unhappy. Until now . . . until this bleak moment in the sun, the first of spring, the last spring ever for Blaise Meredith.

The last spring, the last summer. The butt end of life chewed and sucked dry like a sugar stick, then tossed onto the trash heap. There was the bitterness, the sour taste of failure and disillusion. What of merit could he tally and take with him to the judgment? What would he leave behind, for which men would want to remember him?

He had never fathered a child nor planted a tree, nor set one stone on another for house or monument. He had spent no anger, dispensed no charity. His work would molder anonymously in the archives of the Vatican. Whatever virtue had flowered out of his ministry was sacramental and not personal. No poor would bless him for their bread, no sick for their courage, no sinners for their salvation. He had done everything that was demanded of him, yet he would die empty and within a month his name would be a blown dust on the desert of the centuries.

Suddenly he was terrified. A cold sweat broke out on his body. His hands began to tremble and a group of children bouncing a ball near the bench edged away from the gaunt, gray-faced cleric who sat staring with blind eyes across the shimmering water of the pond.

The rigors passed slowly. The terror abated and he was calm again. Reason took hold of him and he began to think how he should order his life for the time left to him.

When he had become ill in Rome, when the Italian physicians had made their first, tentative diagnosis, his instinctive decision had been to return to London. If he must be condemned, he preferred to have the sentence read in his own tongue. If his time must be shortened, then he wanted to spend the last of it in the soft air of England, to walk the downs and the beechwoods and hear the elegiac song of the nightingales in the shadow of old churches, where Death was more familiar and more friendly because the English had spent centuries teaching him politeness.

In Italy, death was harsh, dramatic—a grand opera exit, with wailing chorus and tossing plumes and black baroque hearses trundling past stucco palaces to the marble vaults of the Campo Santo. Here in England it had a gentler aspect—the obits murmured discreetly in a Norman nave, the grave opened in mown grass among weathered headstones, the libations poured in the oak-beamed pub which stood opposite the lich-gate.

Now, this, too, was proved an illusion, a pathetic fallacy, no armor at all against the gray insidious enemy entrenched in his own belly. He could not escape it, any more than he could flee the conviction of his own failure as a priest and as a man.

What then? Submit to the knife? Cut short the agony, truncate the fear and the loneliness to a manageable limit? Would not this be a new failure, a kind of suicide that the moralists might justify, but conscience could never quite condone? He had enough debts already to bring to the reckoning; this last might make him altogether bankrupt.

Go back to work? Sit at the old desk under the coffered ceiling in the Palace of Congregations in Rome. Open up the vast folios where the lives and works and writings of long-dead candidates for canonization were recorded in the script of a thousand clerks. Examine them, dissect them, analyze and notate. Call their virtues in question and cast new doubts on the wonders attributed to them. Make new notes in a new script. To what end? That one more candidate for canonical honors might be rejected because he had been less than heroic, or less than wise in his virtues. Or that half a century hence, two centuries maybe, a new Pope might proclaim in St. Peter's that a new saint had been added to the Calendar.

Did they care, these dead ones, what he wrote of them? Did

they care whether a new statue were permitted to wear an aureole, or whether the printers circulated a million little cards with their faces on the front and their virtues listed on the back? Did they smile on their bland biographers or frown on their official detractors? They had died and been judged long since, as he must die and soon be judged. The rest was all addendum, postscript and dispensable. A new cultus, a new pilgrimage, a new mass in the liturgy would touch them not at all. Blaise Meredith, priest, philosopher, canonist, might work twelve months or twelve years on their records without adding a jot to their felicity, or a single pain to their damnation.

Yet this was his work and he must do it, because it lay ready to his hand—and because he was too tired and too ill to begin any other. He would say mass each day, work out his daily stint at the Palace of Congregations, preach occasionally in the English Church, hear confessions for a colleague on vacation, go back each night to his small apartment at the Porta Angelica, read a little, say his office, then struggle through the restless nights to the sour morning. For twelve months. Then he would be dead. For a week they would name him in the masses . . . "our brother Blaise Meredith"; then he would join the anonymous and the forgotten in the general remembrance . . . "all the faithful departed."

It was cold in the park now. The lovers were brushing the grass off their coats and the girls were smoothing down their skirts. The children were dragging listlessly down the paths in the wake of scolding parents. The swans were ruffling back to the shelter of the islets, to the drone of peak-hour traffic.

Time to go. Time for Monsignor Blaise Meredith to pack his troubled thoughts and compose his thin features into a courteous smile for the Administrator's tea at Westminster. The English were a civil and tolerant people. They expected a man to work out his salvation soberly or damn himself with discretion, to hold his liquor like a gentleman and keep his troubles to himself. They were suspicious of saints and chary of mystics, and they more than half-believed that God Almighty felt the same way. Even in the hour of his private Gethsemane, Meredith was glad of the convention that would force him to forget himself and attend to the chatter of his colleagues.

He got up stiffly from the bench, stood a long moment as if unsure of his own tenancy in the body, then walked steadily down toward Brompton Road.

THE TROUBLE

J. F. Powers

We watched at the window all that afternoon. Old Gramma came out of her room and said, "Now you kids get away from there this minute." And we would until she went back to her room. We could hear her old rocking chair creak when she got up or sat down, and so we always ran away from the window before she came into the room to see if we were minding her good or looking out. Except once she went back to her room and didn't sit down, or maybe she did and got up easy so the chair didn't creak, or maybe we got our signals mixed, because she caught us all there and shooed us away and pulled down the green shade. The next time we were real sure she wasn't foxing us before we went to the window and lifted the shade just enough to peek out.

It was like waiting for rats as big as cats to run out from under a tenement so you could pick them off with a .22. Rats are about the biggest live game you can find in ordinary times and you see more of them than white folks in our neighborhood —in ordinary times. But the rats we waited for today were white ones, and they were doing most of the shooting themselves. Sometimes some coloreds would come by with guns, but not often; they mostly had clubs. This morning we'd seen the whites catch up with a shot-in-the-leg colored and throw bricks and stones at his black head until it got all red and he was dead. I could still see the wet places in the alley. That's why we kept looking out the window. We wanted to see some whites get killed for a change, but we didn't much think we would, and I guess what we really expected to see was nothing, or maybe them killing another colored.

There was a rumpus downstairs in front, and I could hear

a mess of people tramping up the stairs. They kept on coming after the second floor and my sister Carrie, my twin, said maybe they were whites come to get *us* because we saw what they did to the shot-in-the-leg colored in the alley. I was scared for a minute, I admit, but when I heard their voices plainer I knew they were coloreds and it was all right, only I didn't see why there were so many of them.

Then I got scared again, only different now, empty scared all over, when they came down the hall on our floor, not stopping at anybody else's door. And then there they were, banging on our door, of all the doors in the building. They tried to come right on in, but the door was locked.

Old Gramma was the one locked it, and she said she'd clean house if one of us kids so much as looked at the knob even, and she threw the key down her neck somewhere. I went and told her that was our door the people were pounding on and where was the key. She reached down her neck and there was the key all right. But she didn't act much like she intended to open the door. She just stood there staring at it like it was somebody alive, saying the litany to the Blessed Virgin: *Mère du Christ, priez pour nous, Secours des chrétiens, priez* . . . Then all of a sudden she was crying; tears were blurry in her old yellow eyes, and she put the key in the lock, her veiny hands shaking, and unlocked the door.

They had Mama in their arms. I forgot all about Old Gramma, but I guess she passed out. Anyway, she was on the floor and a couple of men were picking her up and a couple of women were saying, "Put her here, put her there." I wasn't worried as much about Old Gramma as I was about Mama.

A bone—God, it made me sick—had poked through the flesh of Mama's arm, all bloody like a sharp stick, and something terrible was wrong with her chest. I couldn't look any more and Carrie was screaming. That started me crying. Tears got in the way, but I could see the baby, one and a half, and brother George, four and a half, and they had their eyes wide-open at what they saw and weren't crying a bit, too young to know what the hell.

They put Old Gramma in her room on the cot and closed the door on her and some old woman friend of hers that kept dipping a handkerchief in cold water and laying it on Old Gramma's head. They put Mama on the bed in the room where everybody was standing around and talking lower and lower until pretty soon they were just whispering.

Somebody came in with a doctor, a colored one, and he had a little black bag like they have in the movies. I don't think our family ever had a doctor come to see us before. Maybe before I was born Mama and Daddy did. I heard the doctor tell Mr. Purvine, that works in the same mill Daddy does, only the night shift, that he ought to set the bone, but honest to God he thought he might as well wait, as he didn't want to hurt Mama if it wasn't going to make any difference.

He wasn't nearly as brisk now with his little black bag as he had been when he came in. He touched Mama's forehead a couple of times and it didn't feel good to him, I guess, because he looked tired after he did it. He held his hand on the wrist of her good arm, but I couldn't tell what this meant from his face. It mustn't have been any worse than the forehead, or maybe his face had nothing to do with what he thought, and I was imagining all this from seeing the shape Mama was in. Finally he said, "I'll try," and he began calling for hot water and other things, and pretty soon Mama was all bandaged up white.

The doctor stepped away from Mama and over to some men and women, six or seven of them now—a lot more had gone —and asked them what had happened. He didn't ask all the questions I wanted to ask—I guess he already knew some of the answers—but I did find out Mama was on a street-car coming home from the plant—Mama works now and we're saving for a cranberry farm—when the riot broke out in that section. Mr. Purvine said he called the mill and told Daddy to come home. But Mr. Purvine said he wasn't going to work tonight himself, the way the riot was spreading and the way the coloreds were getting the worst of it.

"As usual," said a man with glasses on. "The Negroes ought to organize and fight the thing to a finish." The doctor frowned at that. Mr. Purvine said he didn't know. But one woman and another man said that was the right idea.

"If we must die," said the man with glasses on, "let it not be like hogs hunted and penned in an inglorious spot!"

The doctor said, "Yes, we all know that."

But the man with glasses went on, because the others were listening to him, and I was glad he did, because I was listening to him too. "We must meet the common foe; though far outnumbered, let us still be brave, and for their thousand blows deal one deathblow! What, though before us lies the open grave? Like men we'll face the murderous, cowardly pack, pressed to the wall, dying, but—fighting back!"

They all thought it was fine, and a woman said that it was poetry, and I thought if that is what it is I know what I want to be now—a poetryman. I asked the man with glasses on if that was his poetry, though I did not think it was for some reason, and the men and woman all looked at me like they were surprised to see me there and like I ought not to hear such things—except the man with glasses on, and he said, No, son, it was not his poetry; he wished it was, but it was Claude McKay's, a Negro, and I could find it in the public library. I decided I would go to the public library when the riot was over, and it was the first time in my life I ever thought of the public library the way I did then.

They all left about this time, except the doctor and the old woman friend of Old Gramma's. She came out of Old Gramma's room, and when the door opened I saw Old Gramma lying on the cot with her eyes closed. The old woman asked me if I could work a can opener, and I said, "Yes, I can," and she handed me a can of vegetable soup from the shelf. She got a meal together and us kids sat down to eat. Not Carrie, though. She sat in our good chair with her legs under her and her eyes closed. Mama was sleeping and the doctor rolled up the shade at the window and looked out while we ate. I mean brother George and the baby. I couldn't eat. I just drank my glass of water. The old woman said, Here, here, I hadn't ought to let good food go to waste and was that any way to act at the table and I wasn't the first boy in the world to lose his mother.

I wondered was she crazy and I yelled I wasn't going to lose my mother and I looked to see and I was right. Mama was just sleeping and the doctor was there in case she needed him and everything was taken care of and . . . everything. The doctor didn't even turn away from the window when I yelled at the old woman, and I thought at least he'd say I'd wake my mother up shouting that way, or maybe that I was right and the old woman was wrong. I got up from the table and stood by the doctor at the window. He only stayed there a minute more then and went over to feel Mama's wrist again. He did not touch her forehead this time.

Old Gramma came out of her room and said to me, "Was that you raising so much cain in here, boy?"

I said, "Yes, it was," and just when I was going to tell her what the old woman said about losing Mama I couldn't. I didn't want to hear it out loud again. I didn't even want to think it in my mind.

Old Gramma went over and gazed down at Mama. She turned away quickly and told the old woman, "Please, I'll just have a cup of hot water, that's all, I'm so upset." Then she went over to the doctor by the window and whispered something to him and he whispered something back and it must've been only one or two words, because he was looking out the window the next moment.

Old Gramma said she'd be back in a minute and went out the door, slip-slapping down the hall. I went to the window, the evening sun was going down, and I saw Old Gramma come out the back entrance of our building. She crossed the alley and went in the back door of the grocery store.

A lot of racket cut loose about a block up the alley. It was still empty, though. Old Gramma came out of the grocery store with something in a brown bag. She stopped in the middle of the alley and seemed to be watching the orange evening sun going down behind the buildings. The sun got in her hair and somehow under her skin, kind of, and it did a wonderful thing to her. She looked so young for a moment that I saw Mama in her, both of them beautiful New Orleans ladies.

The racket cut loose again, nearer now, and a pack of men came running down the alley, about three dozen whites chasing two coloreds. One of the whites was blowing a bugle—*tan tivvy, tan tivvy, tan tivvy*—like the white folks do when they go fox hunting in the movies or Virginia. I looked down, quick, to see if Old Gramma had enough sense to come inside, and I guess she did because she wasn't there. The two coloreds ran between two buildings, the whites ran after them, and then the alley was quiet again. Old Gramma stepped out, and I watched her stoop and pick up the brown bag that she had dropped before.

Another big noise made her drop it again. A whole smear of men swarmed out of the used-car lot and came galloping down the alley like wild buffaloes. Old Gramma scooted inside our building and the brown bag stayed there in the alley. This time I couldn't believe my eyes; I saw what I thought I'd never see; I saw what us kids had been waiting to see ever since the riot broke out—a man that was fixing to get himself nice and killed. A white man running—running, God Almighty, from about a million coloreds. And he was the one with the tan-tivvy bugle, too. I hoped the coloreds would do the job up right.

The closer the white man came the worse it got for him, because the alley comes to a dead end when it hits our building. All at once—I don't know why—I was praying for that fool white man with the bugle to get away. But I didn't think he had a Chinaman's chance, the way he was going now, and maybe that's what made me pray for him.

Then he did a smart thing. He whipped the bugle over his

shoulder, like you do with a horseshoe for good luck, and it hit the first colored behind him smack in the head, knocking him out, and that slowed up the others. The white man turned into the junk yard behind the furniture warehouse and the Victory Ballroom. Another smart thing, if he used his head. The space between the warehouse and the Victory is just wide enough for a man to run through. It's a long piece to the street, but if he made it there, he'd be safe probably.

The long passageway must've looked too narrow to him, though, because the fool came rushing around the garage next to our building. For a moment he was the only one in the alley. The coloreds had followed him through the junk yard and probably got themselves all tangled up in garbage cans and rusty bed springs and ashpiles. But the white man was a goner just the same. In a minute they'd be coming for him for real. He'd have to run the length of the alley again to get away and the colored have got the best legs.

Then Old Gramma opened our back door and saved him.

I was very glad for the white man, until suddenly I remembered poor Mama all broken to pieces on the bed, and then I was sorry Old Gramma did it. The next moment I was glad again that she did. I understood now I did not care one way or the other about the white man. Now I was thinking of Mama—not of myself. I did not see what difference it could make to Mama if the white man lived or died. It only had something to do with us and him.

Then I got hold of a funny idea. I told myself the trouble is somebody gets cheated or insulted or killed and everybody else tries to make it come out even by cheating and insulting and killing the cheaters and insulters and killers. Only they never do. I did not think they ever would. I told myself that I had a very big idea there, and when the riot was over I would go to the public library and sit in the reading room and think about it. Or I would speak to Old Gramma about it, because it seemed like she had the same big idea and like she had had it a long time, too.

The doctor was standing by me at the window all the time. He said nothing about what Old Gramma did, and now he stepped away from the window and so did I. I guess he felt the same way I did about the white man and that's why he stepped away from the window. The big idea again. He was afraid the coloreds down below would yell up at us, did we see the white man pass by. The coloreds were crazy mad all right. One of them had the white man's bugle and he banged on our door with it. I was worried Old Gramma had forgot to lock it and they might walk right in, and that would be the end of the white man and the big idea.

But Old Gramma pulled another fast one. She ran out into the alley and pointed her old yellow finger in about three wrong directions. In a second the alley was quiet and empty, except for Old Gramma. She walked slowly over against our building, where somebody had kicked the brown bag, and picked it up.

Old Gramma brought the white man right into our room, told him to sit down, and poured herself a cup of hot water. She sipped it and said the white man could leave whenever he wanted to, but it might be better to wait a bit. The white man said he was much obliged, he hated to give us any trouble, and, "Oh, oh, is somebody sick over there?" when he saw Mama, and that he'd just been passing by when a hundred nig—when he was attacked.

Old Gramma sipped her hot water. The doctor turned away from the window and said, "Here they come again," took another look, and said, "No, they're going back." He went over to Mama and held her wrist. I couldn't tell anything about her from his face. She was sleeping just the same. The doctor asked the white man, still standing, to sit down. Carrie only opened her eyes once and closed them. She hadn't changed her position in the good chair. Brother George and the baby stood in a corner with their eyes on the white man. The baby's legs buckled then—she's only been walking about a week—and she collapsed softly to the floor. She worked her way up again without taking her eyes off the white man. He even looked funny and out of place to me in our room. I guess the man for the rent and Father Egan were the only white people come to see us since I could remember; and now it was only the man for the rent since Father Egan died.

The doctor asked the white man did he work or own a business in this neighborhood. The white man said, No, glancing down at his feet, no, he just happened to be passing by when he was suddenly attacked like he said before. The doctor told Old Gramma she might wash Mama's face and neck again with warm water.

There was noise again in the alley—windows breaking and fences being pushed over. The doctor said to the white man, "You could leave now; it's a white mob this time; you'd be safe."

"No," the white man said, "I should say not; I wouldn't be seen with them; they're as bad as the others almost."

"It is quite possible," the doctor said.

Old Gramma asked the white man if he would like a cup of tea.

"Tea? No," he said, "I don't drink tea; I didn't know you drank it."

"I didn't know you knew her," the doctor said, looking at Old Gramma and the white man.

"You colored folks, I mean," the white man said, "Americans, I mean. Me, I don't drink tea—always considered it an English drink and bad for the kidneys."

The doctor did not answer. Old Gramma brought him a cup of tea.

And then Daddy came in. He ran over to Mama and fell down on his knees like he was dead—like seeing Mama with her arm broke and her chest so pushed in killed him on the spot. He lifted his face from the bed and kissed Mama on the lips; and then, Daddy, I could see, was crying—the strongest man in the world was crying with tears in his big dark eyes and coming down the side of his big hard face. Mama called him her John Henry sometimes and there he was, her John Henry, the strongest man, black or white, in the whole damn world, crying.

He put his head down on the bed again. Nobody in the room moved until the baby toddled over to Daddy and patted him on the ear like she wanted to play the games those two make up with her little hands and his big ears and nose. But Daddy didn't move or say anything, if he even knew she was there, and the baby got a blank look in her eyes and walked away from Daddy and sat down, *plump,* on the floor across the room, staring at Daddy and the white man, back and forth, Daddy and the white man.

Daddy got up after a while and walked very slowly across the room and got himself a drink of water at the sink. For the first time he noticed the white man in the room. "Who's he?" he said. "Who's he?" None of us said anything. "Who the hell's he?" Daddy wanted to know, thunder in his throat like there always is when he's extra mad or happy.

The doctor said the white man was Mr. Gorman and went over to Daddy and told him something in a low voice.

"Innocent! What's he doing in this neighborhood then?" Daddy said, loud as before. "What's an *innocent* white man doing in this neighborhood now? Answer me that!" He looked at all of us in the room and none of us that knew what the white man was doing in this neighborhood wanted to explain to Daddy. Old Gramma and the doctor and me—none of us that knew—would tell.

"I was just passing by," the white man said, "as they can tell you."

The scared way he said it almost made me laugh. Was this a white *man,* I asked myself. Alongside Daddy's voice the white man's sounded plain foolish and weak—a little old tug squeaking at a big ocean liner about the right of way. Daddy seemed to forget all about him and began asking the doctor a lot of questions about Mama in a hoarse whisper I couldn't hear very well. Daddy's face got harder and harder and it didn't look like he'd ever crack a smile or shed a tear or anything soft again. Just hard, it got, hard as four spikes.

Old Gramma came and stood by Daddy's side and said she had called the priest when she was downstairs a while ago getting some candles. She was worried that the candles weren't blessed ones. She opened the brown bag then, and that's what was inside—two white candles. I didn't know grocery stores carried them.

Old Gramma went to her room and took down the picture of the Sacred Heart all bleeding and put it on the little table by Mama's bed and set the candles in sticks on each side of it. She lit the candles and it made the Sacred Heart, punctured by the wreath of thorns, look bloodier than ever, and made me think of that song, "To Jesus' Heart All Burning," the kids sing at Our Saviour's on Sundays.

The white man went up to the doctor and said, "I'm a Catholic, too." But the doctor didn't say anything back, only nodded. He probably wasn't one himself, I thought; not many of the race are. Our family wouldn't be if Old Gramma and Mama didn't come from New Orleans, where Catholics are thicker than flies or Baptists.

Daddy got up from the table and said to the white man, "So help me God, mister, I'll kill you in this room if my wife dies!" The baby started crying and the doctor went to Daddy's side and turned him away from the white man, and it wasn't hard to do because now Daddy was kind of limp and didn't look like he remembered anything about the white man or what he said he'd do to him if Mama . . . or anything.

"I'll bet the priest won't show up," Daddy said.

"The priest will come," Old Gramma said. "The priest will always come when you need him; just wait." Her old lips were praying in French.

I hoped he would come like Old Gramma said, but I wasn't so sure. Some of the priests weren't much different from anybody else. They knew how to keep their necks in. Daddy said to Mama once if you only wanted to hear about social justice you could turn on the radio or go to the nearest stadium on the Fourth of July, and there'd be an old white man in a new black suit saying it was a good thing and everybody ought to get some, and if they'd just kick in more they might and, anyway, they'd be saved. One came to Our Saviour's last year, and Father Egan said this is our new assistant and the next Sunday our new assistant was gone—poor health. But Daddy said he was transferred to a church in a white neighborhood because he couldn't stand to save black souls. Father Egan would've come a-flying, riot or no riot, but he was dead now and we didn't know much about the one that took his place.

Then he came, by God; the priest from Our Saviour's came to our room while the riot was going on. Old Gramma got all excited and said over and over she knew the priest would come. He was kind of young and skinny and pale, even for a white man, and he said, "I'm Father Crowe," to everybody in the room and looked around to see who was who.

The doctor introduced himself and said Old Gramma was Old Gramma, Daddy was Daddy, we were the children, that was Mr. Gorman, who was just passing by, and over there was poor Mama. He missed Old Gramma's old woman friend; I guess he didn't know what to call her. The priest went over and took a look at Mama and nodded to the doctor and they went into Old Gramma's room together. The priest had a little black bag, too, and he took it with him. I suppose he was getting ready to give Mama Extreme Unction. I didn't think they would wake her up for Confession or Holy Communion; she was so weak and needed the rest.

Daddy got up from the table mad as a bull and said to the white man, "Remember what I said, mister."

"But why me?" the white man asked. "Just because I'm white?"

Daddy looked over at Mama on the bed and said, "Yeah, just because you're white; yeah, that's why . . ." Old Gramma took Daddy by the arm and steered him over to the table again and he sat down.

The priest and the doctor came out of Old Gramma's room, and right away the priest faced the white man, like they'd been talking about him in Old Gramma's room, and asked him why he didn't go home. The white man said he'd heard some shouting in the alley a while ago that didn't sound so good to him and he didn't think it was safe yet and that was why.

"I see," the priest said.

"I'm a Catholic too, Father," the white man said.

"That's the trouble," the priest said.

The priest took some cotton from his little black bag, dipped his fingers in holy oil, and made the sign of the cross on Mama's eyes, nose, ears, mouth and hands, rubbing the oil off with the cotton, and said prayers in Latin all the time he was doing it.

"I want you all to kneel down now," the priest said, "and we'll say a rosary. But we mustn't say it too loud because she is sleeping."

We all knelt down except the baby and Carrie. Carrie said she'd never kneel down to God again. "Now Carrie," Old Gramma said, almost crying. She told Carrie it was for poor Mama and wouldn't Carrie kneel down if it was for poor Mama?

"No!" Carrie said. "It must be a white God too!" Then she began crying and she did kneel down after all.

Even the white man knelt down and the doctor and the old woman friend of Old Gramma's, a solid Baptist if I ever saw one, and we all said the rosary of the five sorrowful mysteries.

Afterwards the white man said to the priest, "Do you mind if I leave when you do, Father?" The priest didn't answer, and the white man said, "I think I'll be leaving now, Father. I wonder if you'd be going my way?"

The priest finally said, "All right, all right, come along. You won't be the first one to hide behind a Roman collar."

The white man said, "I'm sure I don't know what you mean by that, Father." The priest didn't hear him, I guess, or want to explain, because he went over to Mama's bed.

The priest knelt once more by Mama and said a prayer in Latin out loud and made the sign of the cross over Mama: *In nomine Patris et Filii et Spiritus Sancti.* He looked closer at Mama and motioned to the doctor. The doctor stepped over to the bed, felt Mama's wrist, put his head to her chest, where it wasn't pushed in, and stood up slowly.

Daddy and all of us had been watching the doctor when the priest motioned him over, and now Daddy got up from the table, kicking the chair over he got up so fast, and ran to the bed. Shaking all over, he sank to his knees, and I believe he must've been crying again, although I thought he never would again and his head was down and I couldn't see for sure.

I began to get an awful bulging pain in my stomach. The doctor left the bed and grabbed the white man by the arm and was taking him to the door when Daddy jumped up, like he knew where they were going, and said, "Wait a minute, mister!"

The doctor and the white man stopped at the door. Daddy walked draggily over to them and stood in front of the white man, took a deep breath, and said in the stillest kind of whisper, "I wouldn't touch you." That was all. He moved slowly back to Mama's bed and his big shoulders were sagged down like I never saw them before.

Old Gramma said, *"Jesus!"* and stumbled down on her knees by Mama. Then the awful bulging pain in my stomach exploded, and I knew that Mama wasn't just sleeping now, and I couldn't breathe for a long while, and then when I finally could I was crying like the baby and brother George, and so was Carrie.

THE TRIAL OF ST. THOMAS MORE

Robert Bolt

—NORFOLK (*Takes refuge behind a rigorously official manner*)
Sir Thomas More, you are called before us here at the Hall of
Westminster to answer charge of High Treason. Nevertheless,
and though you have heinously offended the King's Majesty,
we hope if you will even now forthink and repent of your
obstinate opinions, you may still taste his gracious pardon.

—MORE My lords, I thank you. Howbeit I make my petition
to Almighty God that He will keep me in this, my honest
mind, to the last hour that I shall live. . . . As for the matters
you may charge me with, I fear, from my present weakness,
that neither my wit nor my memory will serve to make suf-
ficient answers. . . . I should be glad to sit down.

—NORFOLK Be seated. Master Secretary Cromwell, have you
the charge?

—CROMWELL I have, my lord.

—NORFOLK Then read the charge.

—CROMWELL (*Formally*) That you did conspire traitorously
and maliciously to deny and deprive our liege lord Henry of his
undoubted certain title, Supreme Head of the Church in
England.

—MORE (*With surprise, shock, and indignation*) But I have
never denied this title!

—CROMWELL You refused the oath tendered to you at the
Tower and elsewhere—

—MORE (*Again shocked and indignant*) Silence is not denial.
And for my silence I am punished, with imprisonment. Why
have I been called again?

(*At this point he is sensing that the trial has been in some way
rigged*)

— NORFOLK   On a charge of High Treason, Sir Thomas.

— CROMWELL   For which the punishment is *not* imprisonment.

— MORE   Death . . . comes for us all, my lords. Yes, even for Kings he comes, to whom amidst all their Royalty and brute strength he will neither kneel nor make them any reverence nor pleasantly desire them to come forth, but roughly grasp them by the very breast and rattle them until they be stark dead! So causing their bodies to be buried in a pit and sending *them* to a judgment . . . whereof at their death their success is uncertain.

— CROMWELL   Treason enough here!

— NORFOLK   The death of Kings is not in question, Sir Thomas.

— MORE   Nor mine, I trust, until I'm proven guilty.

— NORFOLK   (*Leaning forward urgently*) Your life lies in your own hand, Thomas, as it always has.

— MORE   (*Absorbs this*) For our own deaths, my lord, yours and mine, dare we for shame enter the Kingdom with ease, when Our Lord Himself entered with so much pain?

(*And now he faces* CROMWELL, *his eyes sparkling with suspicion*)

— CROMWELL   Now, Sir Thomas, you stand upon your silence.

— MORE   I do.

— CROMWELL   But, Gentlemen of the Jury, there are many kinds of silence. Consider first the silence of a man when he is dead. Let us say we go into the room where he is lying; and let us say it is in the dead of night—there's nothing like darkness for sharpening the ear; and we listen. What do we hear? Silence. What does it betoken, this silence? Nothing. This is silence, pure and simple. But consider another case. Suppose I were to draw a dagger from my sleeve and make to kill the prisoner with it, and suppose their lordships there, instead of crying out for me to stop or crying out for help to stop me, maintained their silence. That *would* betoken! It would betoken a willingness that I should do it, and under the law they would be guilty with me. So silence can, according to circumstances, speak. Consider, now, the circumstances of the prisoner's silence. The oath was put to good and faithful subjects up and down the country and they had declared His Grace's title to be just and good. And when it came to the prisoner he refused. He calls this silence. Yet is there a man in this court, is there a man in this country, who does not *know* Sir Thomas More's opinion of the King's title? Of course not! But how can that be? Because this silence betokened—nay, this silence *was* not silence at all but most eloquent denial.

—MORE   (*With some of the academic's impatience for a shoddy line of reasoning*) Not so, Master Secretary, the maxim is "qui tacet consentire." (*Turns to* COMMON MAN) The maxim of the law is (*Very carefully*) "Silence gives consent." If, therefore, you wish to construe what my silence "betokened," you must construe that I consented, not that I denied.

—CROMWELL   Is that what the world in fact construes from it? Do you pretend that is what you *wish* the world to construe from it?

—MORE   The world must construe according to its wits. This Court must construe according to the law.

—CROMWELL   I put it to the Court that the prisoner is perverting the law—making smoky what should be a clear light to discover to the Court his own wrongdoing!

(CROMWELL'S *official indignation is slipping into genuine anger and* MORE *responds*)

—MORE   The law is not a "light" for you or any man to see by; the law is not an instrument of any kind. (*To the* FOREMAN) The law is a causeway upon which, so long as he keeps to it, a citizen may walk safely. (*Earnestly addressing him*) In matters of conscience—

—CROMWELL   (*Smiling bitterly*) The conscience, the conscience . . .

—MORE   (*Turning*) The word is not familiar to you?

—CROMWELL   By God, too familiar! I am very used to hear it in the mouths of criminals!

—MORE I am used to hear bad men misuse the name of God, yet God exists. (*Turning back*) In matters of conscience, the loyal subject is more bounden to be loyal *to* his conscience than to any other thing.

—CROMWELL (*Breathing hard; straight at* MORE) And so provide a noble motive for his frivolous self-conceit!

—MORE (*Earnestly*) It is not so, Master Cromwell—very and pure necessity for respect of my own soul.

—CROMWELL Your own self, you mean!

—MORE Yes, a man's soul is his self!

—CROMWELL (*Thrusts his face into* MORE's. *They hate each other and each other's standpoint*) A miserable thing, whatever you call it, that lives like a bat in a Sunday School! A shrill incessant pedagogue about its own salvation—but nothing to say of your place in the State! Under the King! In a great native country!

—MORE (*Not untouched*) Is it my place to say "good" to the State's sickness? Can I help my King by giving him lies when he asks for truth? Will you help England by populating her with liars?

—CROMWELL (*Backs away. His face stiff with malevolence*) My lords, I wish to call (*He raises his voice*) Sir Richard Rich! (*Enter* RICH. *He is now splendidly official, in dress and bearing; even* NORFOLK *is a bit impressed*) Sir Richard. (*Indicating* CRANMER)

—CRANMER (*Proffering Bible*) I do solemnly swear . . .

—RICH I do solemnly swear that the evidence I shall give before the Court shall be the truth, the whole truth, and nothing but the truth.

—CRANMER (*Discreetly*) So help me God, Sir Richard.

—RICH So help me God.

—NORFOLK Take your stand there, Sir Richard.

—CROMWELL Now, Rich, on 12 March, you were at the Tower?

—RICH I was.

—CROMWELL   With what purpose?

—RICH   I was sent to carry away the prisoner's books.

—CROMWELL   Did you talk with the prisoner?

—RICH   Yes.

—CROMWELL   Did you talk about the King's Supremacy of the Church?

—RICH   Yes.

—CROMWELL   What did you say?

—RICH   I said to him: "Supposing there was an Act of Parliament to say that I, Richard Rich, were to be King, would not you, Master More, take me for King?" "That I would," he said, "for then you would be King."

—CROMWELL   Yes?

—RICH   Then he said—

—NORFOLK   (Sharply) The prisoner?

—RICH   Yes, my lord. "But I will put you a higher case," he said. "How if there were an Act of Parliament to say that God should not be God?"

—MORE   This is true; and then you said—

—NORFOLK   Silence! Continue.

—RICH   I said, "Ah, but I will put you a middle case. Parliament has made our King Head of the Church. Why will you not accept him?"

—NORFOLK   (Strung up) Well?

—RICH   Then he said Parliament had no power to do it.

—NORFOLK   Repeat the prisoner's words!

—RICH   He said, "Parliament has not the competence." Or words to that effect.

—CROMWELL   He denied the title?

—RICH   He did.

(All look to MORE, but he looks to RICH)

—MORE   In good faith, Rich, I am sorrier for your perjury than my peril.

—NORFOLK   Do you deny this?

—MORE   Yes! My lords, if I were a man who heeded not the

taking of an oath, you know well I need not to be here. Now I will take an oath! If what Master Rich has said is true, then I pray I may never see God in the face! Which I would not say were it otherwise for anything on earth.

—CROMWELL (*To* FOREMAN, *calmly, technically*) That is not evidence.

—MORE Is it probable—is it probable—that after so long a silence on this, the very point so urgently sought of me, I should open my mind to such a man as that?

—CROMWELL (*To* RICH) Do you wish to modify your testimony?

—RICH No, Secretary.

—MORE There were two other men! Southwell and Palmer!

—CROMWELL Unhappily, Sir Richard Southwell and Master Palmer are both in Ireland on the King's business. (MORE *gestures helplessly*) It has no bearing. I have their depositions here in which the Court will see they state that being busy with the prisoner's books they did not hear what was said.

(*Hands deposition to* FOREMAN, *who examines it with much seriousness*)

—MORE If I had really said this is it not obvious he would instantly have called these men to witness?

—CROMWELL Sir Richard, have you anything to add?

—RICH Nothing, Mr. Secretary.

—NORFOLK Sir Thomas?

—MORE (*Looking at* FOREMAN) To what purpose? I am a dead man. (*To* CROMWELL) You have your desire of me. What you have hunted me for is not my actions, but the thoughts of my heart. It is a long road you have opened. For first men will disclaim their hearts and presently they will have no hearts. God help the people whose Statesmen walk your road.

—NORFOLK Then the witness may withdraw.

(RICH *crosses the stage, watched by* MORE)

—MORE   I *have* one question to ask the witness. (RICH *stops*) That's a chain of office you are wearing. (*Reluctantly* RICH *faces him*) May I see it? (NORFOLK *motions him to approach.* MORE *examines the medallion*) The red dragon. (*To* CROMWELL) What's this?

—CROMWELL   Sir Richard is appointed Attorney-General for Wales.

—MORE   (*Looking into* RICH's *face, with pain and amusement*) For Wales? Why, Richard, it profits a man nothing to give his soul for the whole world. . . . But for Wales!

(*Exit* RICH, *stiff-faced, but infrangibly dignified*)

—CROMWELL   Now I must ask the Court's indulgence! I have a message for the prisoner from the King. (*Urgently*) Sir Thomas, I am empowered to tell you that even now—

—MORE   No, no, it cannot be.

—CROMWELL   The case rests! (NORFOLK *is staring at* MORE) My Lord!

—NORFOLK   The jury will retire and consider the evidence.

—CROMWELL   Considering the evidence it shouldn't be necessary for them to retire. (*Standing over* FOREMAN) Is it necessary?

—FOREMAN   (*Shakes his head*) No, sir!

—NORFOLK   Then is the prisoner guilty or not guilty?

—FOREMAN   Guilty, my lord!

—NORFOLK   (*Leaping to his feet; all rise save* MORE) Prisoner at the bar, you have been found guilty of High Treason. The sentence of the Court—

—MORE   My lord! (NORFOLK *breaks off.* MORE *has a sly smile. From this point to the end of the play his manner is of one who has fulfilled all his obligations and will now consult no interests but his own*) My lord, when *I* was practicing the law, the manner was to ask the prisoner *before* pronouncing the sentence, if he had anything to say.

—NORFOLK   (*Flummoxed*) Have you anything to say?

—MORE   Yes. (*He rises; all others sit*) To avoid this I have taken every path my winding wits would find. Now that the Court has determined to condemn me, God knoweth how, I will discharge my mind . . . concerning my indictment and the King's title. The indictment is grounded in an Act of Parliament which is directly repugnant to the Law of God. The King in Parliament cannot bestow the Supremacy of the Church because it is a Spiritual Supremacy! And more to this the immunity of the Church is promised both in Magna Carta and the King's own Coronation Oath!

—CROMWELL   Now we plainly see that you *are* malicious!

—MORE   Not so, Master Secretary! (*He pauses, and launches, very quietly, ruminatively, into his final stock-taking*) I am the King's true subject, and pray for him and all the realm. . . . I do none harm, I say none harm, I think none harm. And if this be not enough to keep a man alive, in good faith I long not to live. . . . I have, since I came into prison, been several times in such a case that I thought to die within the hour, and I thank Our Lord I was never sorry for it, but rather sorry when it passed. And therefore, my poor body is at the King's pleasure. Would God my death might do him some good. . . . (*With a great flash of scorn and anger*) Nevertheless, it is not for the Supremacy that you have sought my blood—but because I would not bend to the marriage!

(*Immediately the scene change commences, while* NORFOLK *reads the sentence*)

—NORFOLK   Prisoner at the bar, you have been found guilty on the charge of High Treason. The sentence of the Court is that you shall be taken from this Court to the Tower, thence to the place of execution, and there your head shall be stricken from your body, and may God have mercy on your soul!

GODS SEES THE TRUTH BUT WAITS

Leo Tolstoy

In the town of Vladimir lived a young merchant named Ivan
Dmitrich Aksionov. He had two shops and a house of his own.

Aksionov was a handsome, fair-haired, curly-headed fellow,
full of fun, and very fond of singing. When quite a young man
he had been given to drink, and was riotous when he had had
too much; but after he married he gave up drinking, except
now and then.

One summer Aksionov was going to the Nizhny Fair, and
as he bade good-bye to his family, his wife said to him, "Ivan
Dmitrich, do not start to-day; I have had a bad dream about
you."

Aksionov laughed, and said, "You are afraid that when I get
to the fair I shall go on a spree."

His wife replied: "I do not know what I am afraid of; all I
know is that I had a bad dream. I dreamt you returned from
the town, and when you took off your cap I saw that your
hair was quite grey."

Aksionov laughed. "That's a lucky sign," said he. "See if I
don't sell out all my goods, and bring you some presents from
the fair."

So he said good-bye to his family, and drove away.

When he had travelled half-way, he met a merchant whom
he knew, and they put up at the same inn for the night.
They had some tea together, and then went to bed in adjoining
rooms.

It was not Aksionov's habit to sleep late, and wishing to
travel while it was still cool, he aroused his driver before dawn,
and told him to put in the horses.

Then he made his way across to the landlord of the inn (who

lived in a cottage at the back), paid his bill, and continued his journey.

When he had gone about twenty-five miles, he stopped for the horses to be fed. Aksionov rested awhile in the passage of the inn, then he stepped out onto the porch, and, ordering a samovar to be heated, got out his guitar and began to play.

Suddenly a troika drove up with tinkling bells and an official alighted, followed by two soldiers. He came to Aksionov and began to question him, asking him who he was and whence he came. Aksionov answered him fully, and said, "Won't you have some tea with me?" But the official went on cross-questioning him and asking him, "Where did you spend last night? Were you alone, or with a fellow-merchant? Did you see the other merchant this morning? Why did you leave the inn before dawn?"

Aksionov wondered why he was asked all these questions, but he described all that had happened, and then added, "Why do you cross-question me as if I were a thief or a robber? I am travelling on business of my own, and there is no need to question me."

Then the official, calling the soldiers, said, "I am the police-officer of this district, and I question you because the merchant with whom you spent last night has been found with his throat cut. We must search your things."

They entered the house. The soldiers and the police-officer unstrapped Aksionov's luggage and searched it. Suddenly the officer drew a knife out of a bag, crying, "Whose knife is this?"

Aksionov looked, and seeing a blood-stained knife taken from his bag, he was frightened.

"How is it there is blood on this knife?"

Aksionov tried to answer, but could hardly utter a word, and only stammered: "I—don't know—not mine."

Then the police-officer said: "This morning the merchant was found in bed with his throat cut. You are the only person who could have done it. The house was locked from the inside, and no one else was there. Here is this blood-stained knife in your bag, and your face and manner betray you! Tell me how you killed him, and how much money you stole?"

Aksionov swore he had not done it; that he had not seen the merchant after they had had tea together; that he had no money except eight thousand rubles of his own, and that the knife was not his. But his voice was broken, his face pale, and he trembled with fear as though he were guilty.

The police-officer ordered the soldiers to bind Aksionov and to put him in the cart. As they tied his feet together and flung him into the cart, Aksionov crossed himself and wept. His money and goods were taken from him, and he was sent to the nearest town and imprisoned there. Enquiries as to his character were made in Vladimir. The merchants and other inhabitants of that town said that in former days he used to drink and waste his time, but that he was a good man. Then the trial came on: he was charged with murdering a merchant from Ryazan, and robbing him of twenty thousand rubles.

His wife was in despair, and did not know what to believe. Her children were all quite small; one was a baby at her breast. Taking them all with her, she went to the town where her husband was in jail. At first she was not allowed to see him; but after much begging, she obtained permission from the officials, and was taken to him. When she saw her husband in prison-dress and in chains, shut up with thieves and criminals, she fell down, and did not come to her senses for a long time. Then she drew her children to her, and sat down near him. She told him of things at home, and asked about what had happened to him. He told her all, and she asked, "What can we do now?"

"We must petition the Czar not to let an innocent man perish."

His wife told him that she had sent a petition to the Czar, but it had not been accepted.

Aksionov did not reply, but only looked downcast.

Then his wife said, "It was not for nothing I dreamt your hair had turned grey. You remember? You should not have started that day." And passing her fingers through his hair, she said: "Vanya dearest, tell your wife the truth; was it not you who did it?"

"So you, too, suspect me!" said Aksionov, and, hiding his face in his hands, he began to weep. Then a soldier came to say that the wife and children must go away; and Aksionov said good-bye to his family for the last time.

When they were gone, Aksionov recalled what had been said, and when he remembered that his wife also had suspected him, he said to himself, "It seems that only God can know the truth; it is to Him alone we must appeal, and from Him alone expect mercy."

And Aksionov wrote no more petitions; gave up all hope, and only prayed to God.

Aksionov was condemned to be flogged and sent to the mines. So he was flogged with a knot, and when the wounds made by the knot were healed, he was driven to Siberia with other convicts.

For twenty-six years Aksionov lived as a convict in Siberia. His hair turned white as snow, and his beard grew long, thin, and grey. All his mirth went; he stooped; he walked slowly; spoke little, and never laughed, but he often prayed.

In prison Aksionov learnt to make boots, and earned a little money, with which he bought *The Lives of the Saints*. He read this book when there was light enough in the prison; and on Sundays in the prison-church he read the lessons and sang in the choir; for his voice was still good.

The prison authorities liked Aksionov for his meekness, and his fellow-prisoners respected him: they called him "Grandfather," and "The Saint." When they wanted to petition the prison authorities about anything, they always made Aksionov their spokesman, and when there were quarrels among the prisoners they came to him to put things right, and to judge the matter.

No news reached Aksionov from his home, and he did not even know if his wife and children were still alive.

One day a fresh gang of convicts came to the prison. In the evening the old prisoners collected round the new ones and asked them what towns or villages they came from, and what they were sentenced for. Among the rest Aksionov sat down near the newcomers, and listened with downcast air to what was said.

One of the new convicts, a tall, strong man of sixty, with a closely-cropped grey beard, was telling the others what he had been arrested for.

"Well, friends," he said, "I only took a horse that was tied to a sledge, and I was arrested and accused of stealing. I said I had only taken it to get home quicker, and had then let it go; besides, the driver was a personal friend of mine. So I said, 'It's all right.' 'No,' said they, 'you stole it.' But how or where I stole it they could not say. I once really did something wrong, and ought by rights to have come here long ago, but that time I was not found out. Now I have been sent here for nothing at all. . . . Eh, but it's lies I'm telling you; I've been to Siberia before, but I did not stay long."

"Where are you from?" asked some one.

"From Vladimir. My family are of that town. My name is Makar, and they also call me Semyonich."

Aksionov raised his head and said: "Tell me, Semyonich, do you know anything of the merchants Aksionov of Vladimir? Are they still alive?"

"Know them? Of course I do. The Aksionovs are rich, though their father is in Siberia: a sinner like ourselves, it seems! As for you, Gran'dad, how did you come here?"

Aksionov did not like to speak of his misfortune. He only sighed, and said, "For my sins I have been in prison these twenty-six years."

"What sins?" asked Makar Semyonich.

But Aksionov only said, "Well, well—I must have deserved it!" He would have said no more, but his companions told the newcomers how Aksionov came to be in Siberia; how some one had killed a merchant, and had put the knife among Aksionov's things, and Aksionov had been unjustly condemned.

When Makar Semyonich heard this, he looked at Aksionov, slapped his own knee, and exclaimed, "Well, this is wonderful! Really wonderful! But how old you've grown, Gran'dad!"

The others asked him why he was so surprised, and where he had seen Aksionov before; but Makar Semyonich did not reply. He only said: "It's wonderful that we should meet here, lads!"

These words made Aksionov wonder whether this man knew who had killed the merchant; so he said, "Perhaps, Semyonich, you have heard of that affair, or maybe you've seen me before?"

"How could I help hearing? The world's full of rumours. But it's a long time ago, and I've forgotten what I heard."

"Perhaps you heard who killed the merchant?" asked Aksionov.

Makar Semyonich laughed, and replied: "It must have been him in whose bag the knife was found! If some one else hid the knife there, 'He's not a thief till he's caught,' as the saying is. How could any one put a knife into your bag while it was under your head? It would surely have woke you up."

When Aksionov heard these words, he felt sure this was the man who had killed the merchant. He rose and went away. All that night Aksionov lay awake. He felt terribly unhappy, and all sorts of images rose in his mind. There was the image of his wife as she was when he parted from her to go to the fair. He saw her as if she were present; her face and her eyes rose before him; he heard her speak and laugh. Then he saw his children, quite little, as they were at that time: one with a little cloak on, another at his mother's breast. And then he remembered himself as he used to be—young and merry. He remembered how he sat playing the guitar on the porch of the inn where he was arrested, and how free from care he had been. He saw, in his mind, the place where he was flogged, the executioner, and the people standing around; the chains, the convicts, all the twenty-six years of his prison life, and his premature old age. The thought of it all made him so wretched that he was ready to kill himself.

"And it's all that villain's doing!" thought Aksionov. And his anger was so great against Makar Semyonich that he longed for vengeance, even if he himself should perish for it. He kept repeating prayers all night, but could get no peace. During the day he did not go near Makar Semyonich, nor even look at him.

A fortnight passed in this way. Aksionov could not sleep at night, and was so miserable that he did not know what to do.

One night as he was walking about the prison he noticed some earth that came rolling out from under one of the shelves on which the prisoners slept. He stopped to see what it was. Suddenly Makar Semyonich crept out from under the shelf, and looked up at Aksionov with frightened face. Aksionov tried to pass without looking at him, but Makar seized his hand and told him that he had dug a hole under the wall, getting rid of the earth by putting it into his high-boots, and emptying it out every day on the road when the prisoners were driven to their work.

"Just you keep quiet, old man, and you shall get out too. If you blab, they'll flog the life out of me, but I will kill you first."

Aksionov trembled with anger as he looked at his enemy. He drew his hand away, saying, "I have no wish to escape, and you have no need to kill me; you killed me long ago! As to telling of you—I may do so or not, as God shall direct."

Next day, when the convicts were led out to work, the convoy soldiers noticed that one or other of the prisoners emptied some earth out of his boots. The prison was searched and the tunnel found. The Governor came and questioned all the prisoners to find out who had dug the hole. They all denied any knowledge of it. Those who knew would not betray Makar Semyonich, knowing he would be flogged almost to death. At last the Governor turned to Aksionov whom he knew to be a just man and said:

"You are a truthful old man; tell me, before God, who dug the hole?"

Makar Semyonich stood as if he were quite unconcerned, looking at the Governor and not so much as glancing at Aksionov. Aksionov's lips and hands trembled, and for a long time he could not utter a word. He thought, "Why should I screen him who ruined my life? Let him pay for what I have suffered. But if I tell, they will probably flog the life out of him, and maybe I suspect him wrongly. And, after all, what good would it be to me?"

"Well, old man," repeated the Governor, "tell me the truth: who has been digging under the wall?"

Aksionov glanced at Makar Semyonich, and said, "I cannot say, your honour. It is not God's will that I should tell! Do what you like with me; I am in your hands."

However much the Governor tried, Aksionov would say no more, and so the matter had to be left.

That night, when Aksionov was lying on his bed and just beginning to doze, some one came quietly and sat down on his bed. He peered through the darkness and recognised Makar.

"What more do you want of me?" asked Aksionov.

"Why have you come here?"

Makar Semyonich was silent. So Aksionov sat up and said, "What do you want? Go away, or I will call the guard!"

Makar Semyonich bent close over Aksionov, and whispered, "Ivan Dmitrich, forgive me!"

"What for?" asked Aksionov.

"It was I who killed the merchant and hid the knife among your things. I meant to kill you too, but I heard a noise outside, so I hid the knife in your bag and escaped out of the window."

Aksionov was silent, and did not know what to say. Makar Semyonich slid off the bed-shelf and knelt upon the ground. "Ivan Dmitrich," said he, "forgive me! For the love of God, forgive me! I will confess that it was I who killed the merchant, and you will be released and can go to your home."

"It is easy for you to talk," said Aksionov, "but I have

suffered for you these twenty-six years. Where could I go to now? . . . My wife is dead, and my children have forgotten me. I have nowhere to go. . . ."

Makar Semyonich did not rise, but beat his head on the floor. "Ivan Dmitrich, forgive me!" he cried. "When they flogged me with the knot it was not so hard to bear as it is to see you now . . . yet you had pity on me, and did not tell. For Christ's sake forgive me, wretch that I am!" And he began to sob.

When Aksionov heard him sobbing he, too, began to weep.

"God will forgive you!" said he. "Maybe I am a hundred times worse than you." And at these words his heart grew light, and the longing for home left him. He no longer had any desire to leave the prison, but only hoped for his last hour to come.

In spite of what Aksionov had said, Makar Semyonich confessed his guilt. But when the order for his release came, Aksionov was already dead.

THE LAST NIGHT

Graham Greene

The lieutenant waited till after dark and then he went himself. It would be dangerous to send another man because the news would be around the city in no time that Padre José had been permitted to carry out a religious duty in the prison. It was wiser not to let even the jefe know: one didn't trust one's superiors when one was more successful than they were. He knew the jefe wasn't pleased that he had brought the priest in—an escape would have been better from his point of view.

In the patio he could feel himself watched by a dozen eyes: the children clustered there ready to shout at Padre José if he appeared. He wished he had promised the priest nothing, but he was going to keep his word—because it would be a triumph for that old corrupt God-ridden world if it could show itself superior on any point—whether of courage, truthfulness, justice . . .

Nobody answered his knock: he stood darkly in the patio like a petitioner. Then he knocked again, and a voice called: "A moment. A moment."

Padre José put his face against the bars of his window and said: "Who's there?" He seemed to be fumbling at something near the ground.

"Lieutenant of police."

"Oh," Padre José squeaked. "Excuse me. It is my trousers. In the dark." He seemed to heave at something and there was a sharp crack, as if his belt or braces had given way. Across the patio the children began to squeak: "Padre José. Padre José." When he came to the door he wouldn't look at them, muttering tenderly: "The little devils."

The lieutenant said: "I want you to come up to the police station."

"But I've done nothing. Nothing. I've been so careful."

"Padre José," the children squeaked.

He said imploringly: "If it's anything about a burial, you've been misinformed. I wouldn't even say a prayer."

"Padre José. Padre José."

The lieutenant turned and strode across the patio. He said furiously to the faces at the grille: "Be quiet. Go to bed. At once. Do you hear me?" They dropped out of sight one by one, but immediately the lieutenant's back was turned, they were there again watching.

Padre José said: "Nobody can do anything with those children."

A woman's voice said: "Where are you, José?"

"Here, my dear. It is the police."

A huge woman in a white night-dress came billowing out at them: it wasn't much after seven: perhaps she lived, the lieutenant thought, in that dress—perhaps she lived in bed. He said: "Your husband," dwelling on the term with satisfaction, "your husband is wanted at the station."

"Who says so?"

"I do."

"He's done nothing."

"I was just saying, my dear . . ."

"Be quiet. Leave the talking to me."

"You can both stop jabbering," the lieutenant said. "You're wanted at the station to see a man—a priest. He wants to confess."

"To me?"

"Yes. There's no one else."

"Poor man," Padre José said. His little pink eyes swept the patio. "Poor man." He shifted uneasily, and took a furtive look at the sky where the constellations wheeled.

"You won't go," the woman said.

"It's against the law, isn't it?" Padre José asked.

"You needn't trouble about that."

"Oh, we needn't, eh?" the woman said. "I can see through you. You don't want my husband to be let alone. You want to trick him. I know your work. You get people to ask him to say prayers—he's a kind man. But I'd have you remember this—he's a pensioner of the government."

The lieutenant said slowly: "This priest—he has been working for years secretly—for *your* Church. We've caught him and, of course, he'll be shot tomorrow. He's not a bad man, and I told him he could see you. He seems to think it will do him good."

"I know him," the woman interrupted, "he's a drunkard. That's all he is."

"Poor man," Padre José said. "He tried to hide here once."

"I promise you," the lieutenant said, "nobody shall know."

"Nobody know?" the woman cackled. "Why it will be all over town. Look at those children there. They never leave José alone." She went on: "There'll be no end to it—everybody wanting to confess, and the Governor will hear of it, and the pension will be stopped."

"Perhaps, my dear," José said, "it's my duty . . ."

"You aren't a priest any more," the woman said, "you're my husband." She used a coarse word. "That's your duty now."

The lieutenant listened to them with acid satisfaction. It was like rediscovering an old belief. He said: "I can't wait here while you argue. Are you going to come with me?"

"He can't make you," the woman said.

"My dear, it's only that . . . well . . . I *am* a priest."

"A priest," the woman cackled, "you a priest!" She went off into a peal of laughter, which was taken tentatively up by the children at the window. Padre José put his fingers up to his pink eyes as if they hurt. He said: "My dear . . ." and the laughter went on.

"Are you coming?"

Padre José made a despairing gesture—as much as to say, what does one more failure matter in a life like this? He said: "I don't think it's—possible."

"Very well," the lieutenant said. He turned abruptly—he
hadn't any more time to waste on mercy, and heard Padre
José's voice speak imploringly: "Tell him I shall pray." The
children had gained confidence: one of them called sharply:
"Come to bed, José." and the lieutenant laughed once—a poor
unconvincing addition to the general laughter which now surrounded Padre José, ringing up all round to the disciplined
constellations he had once known by name.

The lieutenant opened the cell door: it was very dark inside:
he shut the door carefully behind him and locked it, keeping his
hand on his gun. He said: "He won't come."

A little bunched figure in the darkness was the priest. He
crouched on the floor like a child playing. He said: "You
mean—not tonight?"

"I mean he won't come at all."

There was silence for some while, if you could talk of silence
where there was always the drill-drill of mosquitoes and the
little crackling explosion of beetles against the wall. At last
the priest said: "He was afraid, I suppose. . . ."

"His wife wouldn't let him come."

"Poor man." He tried to giggle, but no sound could have
been more miserable than the half-hearted attempt. His head
dropped between his knees: he looked as if he had abandoned
everything, and been abandoned.

The lieutenant said: "You had better know everything.
You've been tried and found guilty."

"Couldn't I have been present at my own trial?"

"No." He was silent, preparing an attitude. Then he asked
with a kind of false jauntiness: "And when, if I may ask . . . ?"

"Tomorrow." The promptness and brevity of the reply called
his bluff. His head went down again and he seemed, as far as it
was possible to see in the dark, to be biting his nails.

The lieutenant said: "It's bad being alone on a night like
this. If you would like to be transferred to the common cell . . ."

"No, no. I'd rather be alone. I've plenty to do." His voice

failed, as though he had a heavy cold. He wheezed: "So much to think about."

"I should like to do something for you," the lieutenant said. "I've brought you some brandy."

"Against the law?"

"Yes."

"It's very good of you." He took the small flask. "You wouldn't need this, I dare say. But I've always been afraid of pain."

"We have to die some time," the lieutenant said. "It doesn't seem to matter so much when."

"You're a good man. You've got nothing to be afraid of."

"You have such odd ideas," the lieutenant complained. He said: "Sometimes I feel you're just trying to talk me round."

"Round to what?"

"Oh, to letting you escape perhaps—or to believing in the Holy Catholic Church, the communion of saints . . . how does that stuff go?"

"The forgiveness of sins."

"You don't believe in that, do you?"

"Oh, yes, I believe," the little man said obstinately.

"Then what are you worried about?"

"I'm not ignorant, you see. I've always known what I've been doing. And I can't absolve myself."

"Would Padre José coming here have made all that difference?"

He had to wait a long while for his answer, and then he didn't understand it when it came: "Another man . . . it makes it easier . . ."

"Is there nothing more I can do for you?"

"No. Nothing."

The lieutenant reopened the door, mechanically putting his hand again upon his revolver: he felt moody, as though now that the last priest was under lock and key there was nothing left to think about. The spring of action seemed to be broken. He looked back on the weeks of hunting as a happy time which was over now for ever. He felt without a purpose, as if life had drained out of the world. He said with bitter kindness (he couldn't summon up any hate of the small hollow man): "Try to sleep."

He was closing the door when a scared voice spoke. "Lieutenant."

"Yes."

"You've seen people shot. People like me."

"Yes."

"Does the pain go on—a long time?"

"No, no. A second," he said roughly, and closed the door, and picked his way back across the whitewashed yard. He went into the office: the pictures of the priest and the gunman were still pinned up on the wall: he tore them down—they would never be wanted again. Then he sat at the desk and put his head upon his hands and fell asleep with utter weariness. He couldn't remember afterwards anything of his dreams except laughter, laughter all the time, and a long passage in which he could find no door.

The priest sat on the floor, holding the brandy flask. Presently he unscrewed the cap and put his mouth to it. The spirit didn't do a thing to him: It might have been water. He put it down again and began some kind of general confession, speaking in a whisper. He said: "I have committed fornication." The formal phrase meant nothing at all: it was like a sentence in a newspaper: you couldn't feel repentance over a thing like that. He started again: "I have lain with a woman," and tried to imagine the other priest asking him: "How many times? Was she married?" "No." Without thinking what he was doing, he took another drink of brandy.

As the liquid touched his tongue he remembered his child, coming in out of the glare: the sullen unhappy knowledgeable face. He said: "O God, help her. Damn me, I deserve it, but let her live for ever." This was the love he should have felt for every soul in the world: all the fear and the wish to save concentrated unjustly on the one child. He began to weep:

it was as if he had to watch her drown slowly from the shore because he had forgotten how to swim. He thought: This is what I should feel all the time for everyone, and he tried to turn his brain away towards the half-caste, the lieutenant, even a dentist he had once sat with for a few minutes, the child at the banana station, calling up a long succession of faces, pushing at his attention as if it were a heavy door which wouldn't budge. For those were all in danger too. He prayed: "God help them," but in the moment of prayer he switched back to his child beside the rubbish-dump, and he knew it was only for her that he prayed. Another failure.

After a while he began again: "I have been drunk—I don't know how many times; there isn't a duty I haven't neglected; I have been guilty of pride, lack of charity . . ." The words were becoming formal again, meaning nothing. He had no confessor to turn his mind away from the formula to fact.

He took another drink of brandy, and getting up with pain because of his cramp, he moved to the door and looked through the bars at the hot moony square. He could see the police asleep in their hammocks, and one man who couldn't sleep lazily rocking up and down, up and down. There was an odd silence everywhere, even in the other cells: it was as if the whole world had tactfully turned its back to avoid seeing him die. He felt his way back along the wall to the farthest corner and sat down with the flask between his knees. He thought: If I hadn't been so useless, useless . . . The eight hard hopeless years seemed to him to be only a caricature of service: a few communions, a few confessions, and an endless bad example. He thought: If I had only one soul to offer, so that I could say: Look what I've done. . . . People had died for him: they had deserved a saint, and a tinge of bitterness spread across his mind for their sake that God hadn't thought fit to send them one. Padre José and me, he thought, Padre José and me, and he took a drink again from the brandy flask. He thought of the cold faces of the saints rejecting him.

This night was slower than the last he spent in prison be-

cause he was alone. Only the brandy, which he finished about
two in the morning, gave him any sleep at all. He felt sick
with fear, his stomach ached, and his mouth was dry with the
drink. He began to talk aloud to himself because he couldn't
stand the silence any more. He complained miserably: "It's
all very well . . . for saints," and later: "How does he know it
only lasts a second? How long's a second?": then he began to
cry, beating his head gently against the wall. They had given
a chance to Padre José but they had never given him a chance
at all. Perhaps they had got it all wrong—just because he had
escaped them for such a time. Perhaps they really thought he
would refuse the conditions Padre José had accepted, that he
would refuse to marry, that he was proud. Perhaps if he
suggested it himself, he would escape yet. The hope calmed
him for awhile, and he fell asleep with his head against the
wall.

He had a curious dream. He dreamed he was sitting at a
café table in front of the high altar of the cathedral. About six
dishes were spread before him, and he was eating hungrily.
There was a smell of incense and an odd sense of elation.
The dishes—like all food in dreams—did not taste of much, but
he had a sense that when he had finished them, he would
have the best dish of all. A priest passed to and fro before
the altar saying Mass, but he took no notice: the service no
longer seemed to concern him. At last the six plates were
empty; someone out of sight rang the sanctus bell, and the
serving priest knelt before he raised the Host. But *he* sat on,
just waiting, paying no attention to the God over the altar,
as if that was a God for other people and not for him. Then the
glass by his plate began to fill with wine, and looking up he
saw that the child from the banana station was serving him.
She said: "I got it from my father's room."

"You didn't steal it?"

"Not exactly," she said in her careful and precise voice.

He said: "It is very good of you. I had forgotten the code—
what did you call it?"

"Morse."

"That was it. Morse. Three long taps and one short one," and immediately the taps began: the priest by the altar tapped, a whole visible congregation tapped along the aisles—three long and one short. He said: "What is it?"

"News," the child said, watching him with a stern, responsible, and interested gaze.

When he woke up it was dawn. He woke with a huge feeling of hope which suddenly and completely left him at the first sight of the prison yard. It was the morning of his death. He crouched on the floor with the empty brandy flask in his hand trying to remember an act of contrition. "O God, I am sorry and beg pardon for all my sins . . . crucified . . . worthy of Thy dreadful punishments." He was confused, his mind was on other things: it was not the good death for which one always prayed. He caught sight of his own shadow on the cell wall: it had a look of surprise and grotesque unimportance. What a fool he had been to think that he was strong enough to stay when others fled. What an impossible fellow I am, he thought, and how useless. I have done nothing for anybody. I might just as well have never lived. His parents were dead—soon he wouldn't even be a memory—perhaps after all he wasn't really Hell-worthy. Tears poured down his face: he was not at the moment afraid of damnation—even the fear of pain was in the background. He felt only an immense disappointment because he had to go to God empty-handed, with nothing done at all. It seemed to him at that moment that it would have been quite easy to have been a saint. It would only have needed a little self-restraint and a little courage. He felt like someone who has missed happiness by seconds at an appointed place. He knew now that at the end there was only one thing that counted—to be a saint.

NO LITTLE THING

Elizabeth Ann Cooper

He stirred, wanting to wake up; yet it could not be sleep, not
with so much physical awareness in it. Light, transmuted into
a reddish glow, was trying to penetrate his eyelids. He was
crouched down, as if he had been kneeling; his arms were
folded on the bed and his head was cradled on them. He heard
his own whimper of pain, and the early-morning street noises:
a dog let out too early and barking, the clink of milk bottles,
the starting up and stopping of delivery trucks; somewhere
near, a door was closed. But except for sleep, he had no
answer for the dream which embraced him, laying claim to
present consciousness and past remembrance so that there
seemed to be nothing but the dream.

He was running. In flight without direction he passed
through a tangled maze of nightmare streets between strange
buildings deformed by his own terror. He did not know where
he was going. There were kind moments when he did not
know where he had been, and then he could pause, putting his
hand out to a rough hard wall for support, but in the next
instant he must leap away as the wall swayed toward him
with dark windows hanging drunkenly from splintered frames.
Remembering then—or his dream remembered, but would not
tell him—he broke into a run and immediately the drumming
footsteps came on behind him, loud staccato on the concrete
brighter than his own weary lumbering gait. It was the drumming that made his head hurt so; that, and the jolt that went
through his body into his brain with each stride of his own.

Then being cold he shivered, and was back to sensing the
intrusion of light and the numbness of his legs, to hearing
what went on in the street and to feeling his body thrust

forward against the side of the bed, to knowing it was his own pulse, nothing else, that sent the white-hot pain rhythmically through his skull from one side to the other. In a moment he would come to himself, he would be awake, he would enter upon the morning; all in a moment; but great as was his need to break out of the pall of his dream, equally great was his need to hide from something which was waiting to fall on him when he did enter the morning. Still, he must wake; he must, for one thing, straighten up, lift his weight from his chest which was pressed against the bed, making each breath hard to come by; but first, to rest.

Huddling in a doorway trying to suck air into his lungs, he knew it was his own footfall he had heard; silent now, but as soon as he moved on it would dog him again, hounding him like her whisper close to his ear: Wake up, get out, hate, hate, hate you. He peered out from the doorway, searching for landmarks. The city was shapeless, an unformed mass beneath the angles and planes of the night, soft clay oozing into the spaces within the night. *Eloi, Eloi, lama sabachthani.* He stepped out from the doorway and walked slowly now, out of the patch of gloom into the elliptical shine of a street light. Floating high across the nameless street was the yellow rectangle of a lighted window. The street was a dank corridor running between sullied walls and roofed by darkness, a passageway through the ruins. The temple was rebuilt in three days but in the city not one stone was left upon another that had not been thrown down.

A stoop nudged out into the sidewalk. He stumbled against the iron railing, swung himself around it and sat down on the second step. He lit a cigarette. Its tip was a glowing repudiation of the shadows which sheltered him. Get out, turn off that light, I don't want to see you, get out before it gets light, you make me sick; sick to think you ever touched me. He sent the cigarette spinning into the dark-spined gutter, where it lay like the last coal of a holocaust. His father sat in the darkening room, enclosed on three sides by booklined walls and on the fourth by the tall windows which framed the campus and nothing more. Buildings, hedges, trees, and eastward climb of the college. The sky was a brash interloper, covering without discrimination not only the beloved campus but posturing town, farmland, hills, apathy, ignorance, and grossness; it should have stayed over the prairie. Then he turned on a lamp and moved from his red club chair to the swivel chair behind his desk. He looked at his son. Perhaps so, he said; perhaps you have always wanted it; but perhaps this notion of the priesthood is merely a pious adolescent fantasy. The boy protested; had he ever cared for fictions? No, no, the professor conceded rather sadly; you are loyal to reality, and you have a very practical fondness for sticking to the main road.

The floating window brightened until he had to squint against it, and even then the blinding glare probed his eyes, so that finally he buried his face in the crook of his arm. The plodding clop of a horse's hoofs drew near, and the clank of toneless bells, and the rattle of iron wheels on alley cobblestones. So it was Monday morning, and the old Negro with his horse and wagon trailed slowly through the city's alleys gathering up the week-end trash set out by those who paid him to cart it away; or perhaps Thursday morning—he also came around each Thursday morning. His shoulder hurt where her fingers had dug into him, clawing him awake, Get up and get out of here, it's nearly morning. "In a moment, just a moment." Something cruel waited for him when he woke up. Let it wait just a little longer. "Michael." Don't call me that.

Mass. In a moment; when he woke in a moment he had to say Mass. The sleepwalkers would all be there. Michael, Mass. That the cruel and awful thing waiting for him to wake up. Michaelmas daisies, your Uncle Leo would never stoop to calling anything an aster. That, and the pain in his head. It was like having a great blister all across the top of his brain, swelling bigger and bigger, any minute now and it would burst spilling fire down through his body; the slightest move would break it open. He groaned softly, glad to have the dream slipping away from him but afraid to be without it. The dream was like a witch-mother, fearsome but a mother still; better than no mother at all. It was not real, and he did not know how to deal with what was unreal; but for this precious moment of rest it was more desirable than anything real. Reality was his legs numb, his head and chest aching, his back cold, and someone chanting insanely a childish jingle in a man's voice, Mike, Mike, Michael, Mass.

His hat was lying with familiar ease on a table near her door, familiar as though it had lain there before and would again. Before, it had been a door closing he had heard; now it was a door opening, and at the same moment a long breath of cold air sighed across his back. Through the door he had one last glimpse of her lying rigid on her side of the bed with the covers pulled up over her. She didn't turn, or even open her eyes, when she laughed. You'd better hurry or you'll be late for church. "Mike. My God. Mike!"

He brought his head up from his arm and stared at Father Bauer through a gauzy, dancing curtain of pain. "Wha' time's it?" he asked thickly. He touched his lips and they felt swollen and as dry as old paper. "Five to eight," he heard. But: guilty of the body and blood—"I can't say Mass," he croaked.

In agony, he dragged himself to his feet. His numbed legs sagged under him and he had to hunch over the bedpost to keep standing. For a moment all things stopped while he gazed down at the bed and saw that it had not been slept in; but that alone could not give proof to the dream. Then the spread was yanked off and he was being forced down on the bed. "You're sick."

Slumping back against the pillow he said rebelliously, "No," but then he had to say with amazement, "Yes, I think I am." Lifting his head a little, he saw himself stretched out on the bed wearing only trousers and socks, and felt the chill morning air on his naked upper body. Then Father Bauer was covering him with the old quilt. He let his head back on the pillow. The dream crept up to his ear, urging him: Run, you've rested long enough, and he understood it well enough to repeat, "I can't say Mass."

"Don't worry about it, Mike," the older priest said. "I've already had my breakfast, but I'll tell Father Costigan, he'll say the eight. You just rest now. I'm going to call a doctor."

He groped out and caught the hand which was arranging the quilt. "Don't call a doctor," he said, frightened, and sat up. "I'm not that sick—I don't want a doctor."

"You lie down," Father Bauer ordered.

"All right, I will," he bargained. "I'll stay put if you don't call a doctor." He would not let the hand go until he had won a guarded "All right, we'll wait a bit and see how you are." There was something, too, about "back in a minute," so when the door closed again he assumed a posture of sleep which might buy solitude for a little while. It was not easy; lying flat and motionless except for his breathing, he felt himself spinning dizzily—not his whole body, but the responsive self which inhabited some airy chamber of his brain. He opened his eyes and fixed them desperately on the intersection of two cracks in the ceiling plaster, and the spinning ceased. But when he heard the sound of someone approaching his room, he had to close his eyes again, and instantly he was caught in the whirlpool again, revolving slowly at first and then gathering such speed that beneath the quilt his hands had to dig into the bed and hold tightly to keep him from being flung out across the room. Hot sour moisture filled his mouth and trickled burning down his throat so that he almost choked. But craftiness spawned by the dream made him play his game well, and at last the observer went away. At the click of the latch he opened his eyes quickly, and steadied himself again by finding the junction of the two cracks.

He put off thinking ahead; and for the moment he was grateful to the dream for having strength enough left to hold memory at bay. Above all, he must bring his insurgent body to heel, reducing it to obedience. As for the rest, he would trust to his instincts: they seemed to have served him well so far. The humiliation of being sick, the shame of having others think him sick, was more than he could bear; nothing must distract him from the present battle against dizziness, nausea, and pain. But for all his striving after singleness, he could not shed the feeling that outside his awareness another contest was being waged in which he was inexplicably and deeply involved. The feeling carried with it a sense of triumph, as if a crisis had been overcome, or outmaneuvered. What crisis it might be he had no idea (breathe slowly now, and deeper, he commanded himself), until from the open window of the church through the open window of his room he heard the exuberant chiming of small bells: *Sanctus, Sanctus, Sanctus.*

Dream, weakness, and shame all became one: forgotten. Before he had time to think it out, he saw in his mind that the priest on the altar was someone else (Father Costigan, but what did that matter?), someone not himself, and his relief was so great that he sobbed aloud. Some dark thing in the back of his mind rejoiced, praising its own cleverness; shocked, incredulous, he silenced it.

For more than five years, for nearly two thousand mornings, he had gone to the altar as to the source of his being, and he could be turned aside from it no more than could a man lost in the desert be turned aside from the saving waters of a spring. Nearly two thousand days (since that morning when the bishop said: Thou art a priest forever, according to the order of Melchisedech) had had their dawning, for him, when he said *Introibo ad altare Dei*; when he confessed to God, to the Blessed Virgin, to the Apostles Peter and Paul, to all the saints and to the people that he had sinned; when he took up bread and wine, the earth's good fruits, and offered them; when, little by little, he felt himself departing, his personality surrendering to another, until in essence at the moment of miracle he had no name, no marks to identify himself, until he could say without words, I live now, not I, but Christ liveth in me, and

. . . hoc est enim Corpus Meum. Lifting up the Host (for if I be lifted up, I shall draw all things unto Me) and in his heart jubilant: Look: no miracle has ever been like this one; not the lepers cleansed, not Lazarus called from the tomb, not Peter loosed. Not I, but Christ liveth in me . . . this is the chalice of My Blood, the mystery of faith. In this universal here and everlasting now were Bethlehem and Cana, Cenacle and Golgotha and Emmaus. . . .

Only yesterday? Under the cover his hands were wet with perspiration, though his shoulders were cold where the quilt had slipped from them. Thumb and forefinger, without his knowing, had joined together. He was surprised to find himself staring so earnestly at the ceiling and wrenched his gaze away to look about the room. His shirt had been flung across the foot of the bed; the crumpled heap on the nearby chair was his coat. Sickness seemed as distant as the puzzling half-memory he had of some nightmare; yet he lay here trembling while another said his Mass. In almost two thousand days, this had never happened to him. Petulant tears, like those of a child who has arrived too late for the party, were hot in his eyes. His one hour of rapture had been given to another—and he had given it. It would not be so painful if he could discover in himself the residual joy of yesterday's Mass, but he could find it nowhere; as if there had been none. As there had not. Not yesterday, and not for days without number, had he renewed the timeless drama of Calvary with any wonder for the miracle and greatness of it. His mother had said, No, she'd go to an earlier Mass at the cathedral, so she wouldn't have to fast so long. They had the afternoon together, and the evening, until he put her on the ten-forty.

He turned on his side, and something made his shoulder hurt. Propped up on one elbow, he looked at the darkening bruise and the crooked, scabby stripes where Laura Dunne's painted nails had clawed him.

He lunged from the bed, casting the quilt away as though it were polluted, and stood in the middle of the room swaying.

"Ahhh." It was a long, muffled cry. The soul's self-loathing poured out fresh poison, making him ache, and gag. Fists to mouth, he thudded to his knees. All but maddened, he set his will against what had been done, to have it undone. His body hardened with strain; his arms fell to his sides and went rigid; his head pulled back and he gasped open-mouthed for air like a man neck-deep in quicksand. But his will was no match for the past. Suddenly limp, he crumpled to the floor, and the childish tears became a man's bitter weeping. An act of contrition rose as a guttural mumble to his lips, and went no further; his prayer was like a bird in a trap: it flailed its wings in blind frenzy against the steel mesh until it sank down exhausted to await its death. *Eloi, Eloi, lama sabachthani.* Now let someone ask him what it was to be lonely. A man who looks to heaven and finds it empty to his eyes—he is lonely. It was the loneliness of the body with the soul gone from it. I don't understand. My God and my all—I don't understand. Not even Job was punished like this, with sin. Lead us not into temptation, but deliver us from evil. . . .

He stretched his arms out until his hands found the wood beyond the edge of the rug, then pressed his fingers against it until the nails were bent back from the quick, seeking comfort in pain. A thought tempted him, breathing up a spark in hope's ashes; whatever he had done, he had not done with premeditation. He had not gone there last night thinking to possess the pleasure of her body. No, he had gone to see her as she was, rather than as she seemed to be in the weeks when she had lived only in his mind; to hear her speak in her own voice and words rather than in the voice and words his thoughts gave her; to see her real, rather than to see her dreaming, and thus perhaps to be free of her as he had not been free since that afternoon in Sammy Bloom's shop; to— he wept again, because he could not remember what reasons had driven him, could not even be sure there had been reasons. He remembered (oh God, oh my God) the thought of her beauty and grace, and above all the thought of her aliveness; and the puzzle that on the streets and in crowded places he never mistook another for her. He remembered her saying, I want to live forever; and he had almost believed that she would, that there was in her something indestructible, beyond the reach of time and above the irrevocable laws of nature. He had gone to her for that.

He tried again to pray but had no words for it. Was he to say only, I'm sorry, like a child caught in naughtiness? I'm sorry, I won't do it again, please don't be mad at me. He sobbed, croaked a laugh, and sobbed again.

Motionless, suddenly quieted, he thought of Judas. His mind had always boggled at Judas' despair, as at the one genuine mystery recorded in all of time. Judas the traitor was Judas the fool of fools (so it had seemed to him), because he had seen God's forgiveness from God's own hand, yet had gone off with a halter to rot his sorrow with despair. It was no longer such a mystery. The fig tree hearing itself cursed by him who made it, having borne no fruit when the hand was ready to pluck it; damned to barrenness for having been barren under all its proud greenery; withering under the sentence of justice. Judas saw the tree; it stood by the road to Jerusalem. Better not to have been born; better to die now than to add time's agony to eternity's. Poor Judas, who had not loved much.

But—he shivered, taken with a sudden and violent chill; but—brave Judas, obedient to justice if not to mercy. Michael Mundy, *sacerdos in aeternum,* did not have such courage. He got to his hands and knees, lacking strength to lift himself higher, and crawled over to the bed. For an instant he rested; then he hauled himself up to the bed and sat there, wrapping the quilt around his shoulders. The floor, as he looked at it, listed away from him. Outside, muted voices came together for talk, and housewifely heels sounded on pavement as Mass ended and the small steadfast corps of daily communicants came from the church. He had almost two thousand mornings; how many thousands of mornings could some of those people count? He huddled under the quilt, half to hide from their knowing eyes which he felt turned upward to his window—time's agony: the stares, the whispers, the pointing fingers, the contempt, the hatred; and none of it equal to the inner stare, the inner revulsion that no door could close on, even after death.

He looked up from the floor, casting about for something that would lift him out of helplessness—it was as if, mute and paralyzed, he lay at the side of the road, unable to move, unable to call out, so that everyone passed by thinking him dead already; no one stopped to read the plea in his eyes. His glance touched on desk, on high old-fashioned bureau, on armchair and bookcase, table and lamp and yellowing lace curtains. The two-dollar crucifix—his eyes came to rest on that. It so hung that the painted face of the Corpus was turned on him, and the plaster eyes streaked with painted blood gazed into his as if they had been seeking, and at last had found, the face of Judas in the crowd. "But I have loved," Michael whispered, defensively.

He slid to his knees. Through his teeth, making it so by saying it, he recited, "I will wash my hands among the innocent, and will encompass thy altar, oh Lord, that I may hear the voice of praise and tell of all thy wondrous works. For I have loved the beauty of thy house, oh Lord, and the place where thy glory dwells. Take not away my life—" His memory faltered and failed; and he said again, less fiercely, "I have loved the beauty of thy house, and the place where thy glory dwells." And then, "I will wash my hands among the innocent." He thought of his life, spent in a pursuit of joy; joy which, when he glimpsed it, had resided in Laura Dunne. Slowly, laying weight on each word, he said the act of contrition, lingering earnestly over, and repeating, the phrase, "Most of all, because I have offended thee, oh my God, who art all good and deserving of all my love," and as unspoken accompaniment to the words old from childhood was the promise: I will never ask for anything; only keep me safe, and I will ask for nothing. He turned then to a prayer which he had left

long unsaid, surrendering his liberty, his memory, his understanding, and his will—"Give me thy love and thy grace. With
these I am rich enough and desire nothing more."

A moment later he arose and began to dress.

His car was not in the garage which, with the dream still
lurking at the corners of his mind, dismayed but did not
surprise him. Heading down the alley to the street, he wondered if the other fathers had noticed its absence—if so, they
hadn't mentioned it—and where he would find it; he could
guess: somewhere near North Boulevard. But he put thought
of the car from his mind as something insignificant.

He walked over to Jackson to take the streetcar; he wanted
to run; his lifetime fear of time running out on him had never
been greater. But he walked steadily, at measured pace, nodding
to those who greeted him out of their blind, foolish, wasted
respect. Their ignorance of what he was—"Good morning,
Father, nice day"—amazed him no less than had the simple
trust of his fellow priests when he told them that he felt all
right now but would go uptown for an examination. How
could they look at him and not know? How could they go
their ways, these people, as if he had not brought them all
low?

He rode jolting and rocking on the lacquered straw seat,
almost amused by the observation that he was riding to grace
on a streetcar. At Central he got off the streetcar and boarded
a bus. People looked at him for the most part indifferently;
some acknowledged him by a shy smile, a nod, or merely a
glance; one woman's hard stare betrayed hatred; to them all he
wanted to say, I'm sorry, please forgive me for what I've done
to you. He had always been mindful of the oneness of man,
but never so intensely as now; his present concept of it, and his
present terrible involvement in it, gave him a new, frightening,
yet strangely beautiful sense of vision. He felt a quality of
permanence in the thought; it would be with him later for
meditation, when he had the time to give to it.

It was three blocks from where he left the bus to St. Vincent's Church, and again he must walk like a man who could count on a whole day, or even an hour; as if, at every step, there did not grow on him the obsessive dread that at the last moment something was going to happen to block his way, to strike him down with Old Testament vengeance— and there would be justice in it, if something stopped him at the threshold of gratuitous rebirth; no man could claim for himself the right to be called from the tomb. But nothing happened to him, and he saw in that a marvel of mercy.

He went inside the church, seized by apprehension and damning the pride which made him apprehensive. At the foot of the center aisle he dipped his fingers into the font and blessed himself, sinking to one knee in prolonged genuflection while he whispered softly a childhood paean to the Presence in the tabernacle; as he stood up again, his mind repeated, "All praise and all thanksgiving . . ." A late Mass was going on in the north transept. He could not see the altar, but he could see the rapt attention of the worshippers who filled the transept's pews. The main body of the church was dim and still; a few men and women were saying the stations, a few others knelt in prayer. Had he waited until afternoon, there would not have been so many people; he could leave and come back later—it was faint but insistent urging. He leaned against the back of the last pew and listened as it counseled discretion and warned against scandal. No one knows, but even if one person wonders why a priest should rush in here to confession, the wonder will be harm enough. His hands were sweating and he trembled. Then he stifled the inward prophet and walked up the side aisle to the door leading into the monastery.

There was a bell discreetly imbedded in the carved wood at the side of the door and beneath it a small brass plate in need of polishing which read, "Ring for Confessor." He pressed the bell, genuflected again, and retreated down the aisle to kneel in a pew near the confessionals. Head bowed, he recited the

Confiteor and the act of contrition; he could not stop his trembling and he no longer tried. In all his life he had never been afraid of confession. It had always been the easiest, the natural thing to do—but, until now, confession had meant childhood disobedience and impudence, adolescent experiments in profanity; adult uncharitableness or anger. Until now, in the thirtieth year of his life, he had had no vileness to bare.

He heard the merry sparkle of silver bells, once, twice, a third time; in the transept people looked up, gazed before them, bent their heads. Flowing out from them in that instant, and he felt it acutely, was a medley of love, awe, uncertainty, repentance, troubled faith and undoubting faith, worship, inattention, surrender.

The monastery door opened, catching his eye, as the bells signaled the elevation of the chalice. A frail figure engulfed in his white habit, the friar knelt for a moment in prayer; Michael's own confessor. He was struck with panic and resentment—but it was fitting that of all the Dominicans who might have answered the call, it was this one who did so. This old, gentle man who had been his soul's guide and watchman for a year and more. The last bell sounded, and in the transept there was an outbreak of shuffling and coughing and shifting as the tension was broken. The old priest got up, came down the aisle, and with the calm assurance of age, looked at Father Mundy who knelt near the confessional. Then he went into the booth, closed the door behind him, and waited.

Father Mundy remained kneeling a moment longer. A light shone in the confessional, he glanced at its gleam above the door. Then he stood. It came to him suddenly, hideously, that the hard thing would not be to tell what he had done, the hard thing would be to tell that he had found pleasure in it. He looked at the altar and renewed his promise: I will ask for nothing except to be kept safe. Then he went into the confessional and lowered himself to his knees. The old priest reached up and tugged at a knotted string, darkening the booth.

TERESA

Sean O'Faolain

On the platform at Dieppe, at a corner so near the sea and the
boat as to be part of the quay, there stood a small nun, flanked
by three shapeless bags of that old-fashioned kind known as
portmanteaux. Lovely as a black wall-flower, large-eyed by
nature, her eyes were now enormous: for she was looking across
the quays with delight at the sun-blazing confections of houses
on the other side. Now and again an old nun came hobbling up
to her from the busier end of the platform, muttering something that drew a shadow across the lovely face, and then
hobbling away again, head down, to this official and that official,
wavering around like a top as each one hurriedly threw a few
words at her and rushed past. At last the old nun came back to
the novice, with her two hands out in appeal. The novice,
followed by the old nun, at once walked straight down to the
first official she saw and said in clear English:

"Where is the train for Rouen?"

The official glanced at her, then smiled, then bowed, and
said politely, indeed with deference:

"There it is, mademoiselle," and pointed to it.

"Mais, non, non," babbled the old nun. *"Pas aller à Rouen!
Aller à Leesoo!"*

"That's all right, Sister Patrick," said the other. "We change
at Rouen." And taking charge of the situation, she led the still-
protesting nun up to the waiting train, put in the bags, helped
—almost pushed—the old woman before her, and settled herself for the journey. The old woman clambered out again,
red with fluster. Once more she ambushed official after official,
all of whom said a word so like "Wrong" that she insisted on
hauling out her companion.

"Listen, Sister Patrick," begged the novice with saintly patience. "I know the route backwards. It's Dieppe, Rouen, Elbeuf St. Aubin, Serquigny, and then Lisieux. This is the train."

The guard confirmed this, as far as concerned Rouen, and they clambered in at the last moment; but the old woman was still saying that they would never get to "Leesoo," that they would find themselves landed in Paris in the middle of the night, that she had told Mother Mary Mell not to send her, that thirty-one years is too long out of a country for anyone to remember the language, and so on and so on, while the younger nun gazed wide-eyed out of the window at the passing fields.

"Our pilgrimage has begun," she said in a dreamy voice, almost to herself.

"And what's going to be the end of it at this rate?" snapped the old woman. But then she gave a frightened look at the little face before her. The big eyes had lowered. A tremble was flitting across the red lips. The old woman immediately calmed down, laid a rough hand on the novice's knee, and said, gently, "Sure, don't mind me, Sister Teresa. I'm all of a flusther. We're on the road now. Just as you say. When we get to Leesoo, 'twill be all right, a gilly. Saint Teresa will look after you and . . . Look't, I have no sense. We should be eating our lunch."

"I'd love a cup of tea!" said the girl. "I have a raging headache."

"Tut tut," chuckled the old woman, and then she grabbed the girl's flank. "Are ye wearing your double petticoat, Sister Teresa?"

"Yes, Sister," said Teresa, with a blush and a warning look into the corner of the carriage, where an old Frenchman was devouring a roll and slugging red wine.

"Have ye the red-flannel drawers on ye?" demanded the old nun.

"Yes, Sister. Sssh!"

"There's nothing like red flannel next the skin," said the

nun, fiddling with the lunch parcel. "'Tis a touch of cold you've got."

"'Twas the heat down under that deck," said Teresa, and big floods of water entered her eyes. Her chaperone did not notice. "I never saw Dieppe from the sea," she whimpered. "And Mother Mary Mell says that it's lovely from the sea."

"Will ye have egg and cress, or tomato?" asked the old woman, too intent on her own appetite to take notice of anything else. "We earned it," she laughed, with a happy look about her and a countrywoman's smile and nod to the old "Clemenceau" in the corner. He just dug a chunk of his roll off with his penknife, wiped the back of his hand right and left across his mustaches, and with an idle glance at her, opened both mouth and eyes simultaneously to devour the chunk.

The nuns began to nibble their food. Two hens could not have pecked more nimbly or neatly. Their traveling-companion finished his lunch almost before they had well begun. He carefully stowed away his bottle, produced a long cheroot, and began to fill the carriage with smoke. Then, to the dismay of the novice, he leaned across and closed the window tightly. By the time she had finished eating, she had already begun to lean her aching head on her palm. In minute imitation of the Frenchman, the old woman rubbed her mustaches and her beard clean of crumbs, leaned back, closed her eyes, began to eat chocolates and to breathe through her nose. She woke with a start to hear Teresa say to the Frenchman:

"*C'est assez chaud, monsieur. Veuillez bien ouvrir la fenêtre.*"

The old tiger-faced glared, growled, tapped his chest fiercely, poured out a flood of uncompromising French, and leaned back. His sideward glare thereafter was like a cat ready to pounce.

"What's that?" asked the nun apprehensively.

"My head," groaned Teresa.

"Offer it up, girl," advised the old woman. "Offer it up to Saint Teresa for the success of your intention."

"I've offered it up on the boat the whole way over," retorted the novice.

"'Tis a cross," said the old woman easily. "'Tis put on you by Saint Teresa to try you. Suffer it for her sake."

The girl looked at her coldly. Then she observed that they had a second traveling-companion. He was a cavalry officer, who, with more consideration than their "Clemenceau," was walking up and down in the corridor to smoke his pipe. Each time he passed the door he glanced up at his luggage on the rack. She raised her eyes appealingly the next time he passed. He paused, glanced at her, was about to pass on, paused again to look. A tiny gesture of her hand, a widening of her eyes held him. He came in, sat down, looked around him, and stared at her.

"*Monsieur,*" she begged. "*J'ai mal à la tête. La fenêtre. Est-ce nous pouvons l'ouvrir?*"

"With pleasure," he said, in English, stalked over to it and slapped it down.

A raucous argument started up at once between the officer and his fellow-countryman. Sister Patrick sat up, glared at her charge, and drew herself in from the combatants. The argument ended with the abrupt flight of the old man, cursing as he went, a laugh from the officer, and a frightened smile from the novice, accompanied by a glance at her chaperone, who, in the greatest suspicion of the officer, had lowered her head to look crookedly at him, like a duck, out under her coif. He was stroking his little line of mustache and smiling at Teresa. When Patrick slewed full around to survey her charge, Teresa had cast her eyes down demurely on her clasped hands.

Presently the officer got up, and went out to smoke another pipe. Every time he passed, he bowed in to the two nuns. Teresa never looked higher than his knees. When he had passed for about the sixth time, Patrick said:

"Sister, do you realize that officer is bowing to us every two minutes?"

"He is very kind," said the little nun. "Everybody is very kind," she sighed, and began to pray her beads.

But when he passed again, and bowed, the old nun said crossly:

"I believe you're looking at him, Sister Teresa!"

Teresa shook her head sadly and looked out of her big eyes at her chaperone.

"It is sad," she said. "He will be killed in the wars," and her eyes swam with tears.

"And what's that to you?" whispered the old nun angrily.

"He reminds me of my brother, Jim, in the army," said Teresa. "He will be killed on the battlefield too. Oh, let us pray for the pair of them."

The old nun could not refuse to do this, so they prayed together, and when the officer passed, and bowed, and smiled, the two nuns bowed and smiled back, and went on with their prayers for the repose of his soul when he would be killed in the wars. But he was useful at Rouen. He bought them two lovely cartons of *café-au-lait*, with buttered rolls, and showed them where the auto-rail would start. Then for the last time he bowed, and smiled, and went away, and they never saw him again.

II

It was the fading hour of day before their little auto-rail came and took the two travelers (and about eight others) trotting out of Rouen. A light haze of rain began to float down through the air. They passed a village deep in trees. There the first lights were beginning to contest the supremacy of the day. Soon the rain shone in rivulets on the lighted windows of the auto. The other travelers leaned closer together in a kind of animal companionship and chattered in loud voices, as if to keep the night at bay.

"I wonder," murmured Teresa, "what they are doing now back in Saint Anthony's?"

"Ah, yes!" sighed the old nun wearily. "It makes England seem very far away to think of Saint Anthony's now."

"And Dublin?" smiled the novice sadly.

"Ha!" said the old nun, with a yawn that dropped the subject into vacancy. Her youth and her friends were too remote for serious reflection.

"I know what my sisters are doing now in Dublin," whispered Teresa. "Having tea and making plans for the night." And she looked out at the evening shower and the thickening night. "I wish I never came," she said suddenly. "I feel terribly lonely."

"Sssh! Tut tut!" chided the old nun; she had begun to eat more chocolates, and did not want to talk.

"It's all right for you," complained the novice. "You're going to meet your aunt. I'll know nobody in Lisieux. And if I find out there that I have no vocation, what'll I do?"

"Now, now, now," grumbled the old woman, "you know you'll get peace and calm in Leesoo. The saint will reveal your heart to you. You'll quiet down. You'll know that all these scruples of yours mean nothing at all. Sure, we all had them." In spite of herself she became impatient. Her soothing voice gradually took an edge. "And anyway, goodness knows, you were eager enough to come! And let me tell you it isn't every Reverend Mother would let you. And it's not a holiday you're on, Miss. It's thinking of the holy saint you should be, and not of gilly-gooseys in Dublin."

The novice withdrew into herself. She was too tired to pray; from sheer repetition the words were becoming meaningless.

Presently the old nun said, as if she were thinking aloud:

"And even if I have an aunt . . . Ha! . . . I suppose she won't know me."

She stopped again and folded her hands deep into her sleeves.

"Thirty-one years," she mused to the window.

The auto-rail rattled along for several miles. Then, Patrick leaned over and said comfortably:

"A terror for the hot milk at night. She'd drink two pints of it. Sure, 'twas enough to kill a plough-horse."

From then on she kept on letting occasional little gasps of laughter escape her. It was as if somebody tickled her every three minutes. Then, after a protracted giggle out of each side of her mouth, she went off into a beatific sleep and the broad smile never left her face until they stopped abruptly in Lisieux.

As they left the station and emerged on the great square, Teresa cried in delight:

"But it's really a big place!"

Through the rain the little town shone into the station like a prismatic waterfall. She saw a green neon light flitting through the wetness over a hotel door. She saw a vis-à-vis crawling shiningly across the Place, and it made the town seem both cosy and important. But Patrick had flown into a hurry and scurry, fumbling with her umbrella, and clutching her bags, and gazing all around her in a new rush of timidity; the two, in this conflict of absorption, nearly lost one another in the crush. The novice said:

"Oh, Sister Patrick! Couldn't we have one cup of tea in a restaurant before we go to the Hostel?"

"Wh-a-t?" cried Patrick, hunching up her shoulders, and laying her hand on her guimpe like a stage French-woman. "*Mon Pethite, que dites-vous? Du thé? Vous savez bien . . . Vous savez bien que nous . . . Il faut . . . Il faut . . .*" She groaned furiously. "I can't talk French. I told Mother Mary Mell . . . Are you talking about tea? Do you realize, Miss, that you're on a pilgrimage? Gosthering in the middle of the street! Hurry! Hurry!"

They did hurry, under their two black umbrellas, like two ants with top-heavy loads. Suddenly Teresa stopped and sneezed resolutely; once . . . twice . . . four times. Patrick towered over her. She started to gibber at her like a baboon.

"You're after getting a cold on me! That's yourself, and your window, and your fine officer!" Teresa sneezed a fifth time. "Are you sure," demanded Patrick, "that you have the double petticoats?"

The novice's big eyes were directed miserably into a confectioner's window. It was bright with the brightest cakes.

"Dear Sister Patrick!" she wheedled. "Don't you think we could have one small, tiny little cup of tea?"

The nun opened her mouth to say "No," looked at the window, looked at Teresa, and after a struggle said:

"Well! Since you have a cold coming on you, I'll let you have just one hot cup of coffee. Just one, mind you!"

It was warm in the café. Patrick had an eclair. Over their heads a radio kept weaving waltzes that made the novice sway gently on her chair. Patrick had two eclairs. The novice made her coffee last as long as possible. Patrick had a third eclair. Then, in spite of a fleck of cream on her jaw, Patrick's face was unusually forbidding as she looked up and said:

"Well, Miss, I hope you're feeling better now?"

"Thank you very much, Sister," said Teresa, and rose with an air of firm resignation. "We must go to the Hostel."

A bell rang eight o'clock as they emerged. They wasted ten minutes searching for the Hostel, a bald-faced house rising plumb from the pavement. Its brass-tipped, reed-woven half-screens were damply inhospitable. Its closed door and iron grille were shining with the rain. The lay-sister who drew the slide of the grille spoke in unintelligible, provincial French, of which they understood only one word, *"Impossible!"*

"Quoi?" squawked Patrick, clawing the grille, as the slide shot to in her face. "What did that wan say?"

The bell jangled down the hall again. This time the lay-sister was even more emphatic, and therefore even less intelligible, and she became still less intelligible as Patrick hung to the grille and blustered in Franco-English. Teresa firmly pushed her aside, with a calm sanity:

"Vous ne comprenez pas. Tout est bien arrangé. Notre mère a écrit une lettre à votre mère. . . ."

The lay-sister interrupted. She said, *"Trop tard."* She said, *"Huit heures."* She said these words several times. She closed the grille with the slowness of a curiosity that commented on the folly of the two foolish virgins who had come too late. Teresa turned to Patrick, and burst into peals of laughter at the look of horror on her face.

"We're too late!" she cried, joyously. "Now we must go to a hotel!"

Patrick rent her.

"You and your tea! You did it deliberately! Wait until we get back to Mother Mary Mell! I'll tell her you're not fit to be a nun! You're a little flitthermouse! You're a gilly-goosey! What a pilgrim we have in you! There's your answer for you! You're not fit to be a nun! You're a slip! You're a miss! What're we going to do? What'll my aunt say to me? What'll Mother Mary Mell say to me? What's going to happen to us?"

Teresa began to cry. Patrick at once hushed her tirade, un-furled her umbrella (it was as big as a bookmaker's), dragged up two of the bags and set off, in a mouth-buttoned fury, to find a hotel. The rain was now a downpour. Their bags weighted them down. She halted. She gave the girl a look that was worse than a blow, shoved her into a doorway, and said, "Don't stir from there till I come back." She left the bags in her care, and butted out into the rain.

Men kept approaching the door, and seeing the nun, they would stop dead, and push away. At first this merely frightened her for she did not realize her predicament: but suddenly a cistern flushed noisily behind her and she recognized that she was standing in the doorway of a *cabinet*. Clutching her bags, she fled down the street, down a side street, another side street, and halted panting under a café awning.

The old proprietor came out and looked at her, cocked his head to one side, bowed, considered her, smiled, said that it was a bad night, and wiped his indifference on to the tabletop. Then he gazed around him, looked at her again, shrugged, and went indoors. More men passed her, on their way in or out, always pausing, after the first glance, to smile and bow. Twice she got up to fly, wondered whether Patrick would ever find her, sat again on the damp iron chair. A drunken old man with a beard finally put her to flight by taking off his hat, leaning

on the tabletop, and starting a flowery speech. She ran into a
gendarme who was accompanying Sister Patrick down the
street. Patrick threw her two hands up to the sky preparatory to a
tornado of abuse. She was soaked; her guimpe was a rag; her
coif hung around her face like lace. Before she could speak,
Teresa hurled herself on the old woman's breast and sobbed out
all her awful adventures, so that the gendarme and the nun
calmed her with difficulty. They took her bag, then, and led her,
whimpering, to the little pension-pub that Patrick had chosen
for their night's lodging. There Patrick put her into bed, in a
cosy little room all to herself, with red stuff curtains and a dusty-
looking carpet—it was nearly thread-bare—and with her own
two hands Patrick lit a fire, brought an omelette, rolls, and
coffee, and tucked her in for the night; and all the time Patrick
kept begging her pardon for that outburst at the Hostel. What
with the comfort, the kindness, and the vestigial excitement,
the little novice was melted to tears of happiness.

"Our pilgrimage is beginning," she whispered happily to
Patrick. "Isn't it, dear Sister Patrick?"

"'Twill begin in the morning," temporized Patrick. "And
then the saint will smoothen everything out."

Right cheek touched right cheek, and left cheek touched left
cheek, in the way of all nuns kissing. Old fingers laid out her
glossy black hair on the pillow. The light went out. A rough
palm smoothed her forehead. The door clicked. The flames
flickered on the ceiling.

In Kent, at Saint Anthony's, the only sound around the convent at night had been the crackle of twigs in the damp wood,
the hoo-hoo of an owl. Here she heard footsteps in the street
below, an occasional motorcar swishing over the cobbles, the
soft, whispering downfall of April rain. Looking up at the
wavering ceiling, she attended to those sounds, whose tumult,
and whose unfamiliarity, and whose suggestiveness made England and her convent, Dublin and her home, utterly remote—
less part of another country than part of another life. More
than anything else they said, "The pilgrimage has begun!" They

said, "O dear Saint Thérèse, I will leave all things in thy hands."
They said, "O most omnipotent God, I yield all the world to
Thee."

"I want to be a saint!" she cried out, and beat the coverlet
with her palm. And at that she fell asleep, curled up in bed as
softly as a cat.

III

Only the hens were awake as they walked to first Mass at
Saint Pierre. The sun was glittering in the water between the
cobblestones. Teresa felt that she alone possessed the town. She
felt that all things converged on the forthcoming visit to the
shrine. Even the warm prophecy of the steam rising from the
streets and the cloudless whiteness of the sky seemed not something general to everybody in the world, but particular to her
life alone. She whispered to Patrick, "Thérèse is calling! I hear
her!" Patrick nodded, too excited to speak.

After breakfast they began the ritual of Lisieux. Les Buissonnets, the Martin home (Saint Thérèse Martin), was exactly as
they had foreseen it, just like all the photos and descriptions in
biographies of the saint. They saw the "trim lawn in front of
the house," and "the useful kitchen-garden at the back." From
the attic windows there was the expected "distant view over the
plain." Teresa said to Patrick, with a sigh of happiness:

"It was all made for her. If I had lived here, I, too, would have
been a saint!"

Patrick nodded in agreement with the general proposition.
For the novice to say that she could have been a saint was merely
a way of saying that God had chosen one and could as easily
have chosen another.

"'Tis Heaven!" she murmured, and clasped Teresa's hand.

It was the same in the sacristy of the Carmelite convent,
where the saint's hair lies strewn under glass in its reliquary,
and the walls are covered by mementos of those who have paid

honor to her memory—decorations, orders, swords, letters from all over the world. Here, where Patrick became almost incoherent at the prospect of meeting her aunt, thirty-one years after, now a Reverend Mother in the Carmelites, Teresa filled with sadness.

"The folly of the world!" she murmured, sighing again and again. "They honor her now. They did not know the sorrow of her heart while she was alive."

The two touched cheek to cheek again.

A Carmelite lay-sister next led them to the grave of the saint. From that they would go on to the convent proper to meet Patrick's aunt. They began to palpitate in mutual sympathy. The grave calmed them by its simplicity.

When they rose, the aunt stood beside them. Patrick toddled to her with cries of joy. The aged woman, her head a mere skull, her hands bony and ridged, gave no sign of recognition other than to say, "God bless you, my child." Old Patrick drew back like a frightened child. Timidly she introduced the novice. She explained falteringly why they had come.

"She's not sure if she wants to be a nun, Mother."

The Carmelite looked at the novice. She, too, at once, drew back. But the Carmelite smiled to hear the English name, Teresa, and took her hand gently and led her (Patrick following) across the garden to the convent ante-room. On the way she talked of simple things like the budding shrubs and the blessing of the rain. They sat in the ante-room and the Carmelite rang a bell.

They talked of the price of vegetables, until a faint passage of light in one wall drew their eyes to the grille—the last portal of the inner Carmelite hermitage. Behind the grille was a gauze, and presently Teresa's eyes made out, behind the gauze, a still face from which the gauze had eroded all recognizable character. All she could see was the vaguest outline of a countenance. As if she realized in that second how the discipline of the Order must have likewise eroded from the little girl of Les

Buissonnets all human emotion, and in a flash of understanding knew what sacrifice really means, she flung herself at the Carmelite's knees and cried out hysterically:

"*Ma mère!* I have no vocation!"

Patrick intervened hurriedly.

"Pay no heed to her. She's upset and sick in herself. The child doesn't know what she wants."

The aged Carmelite waved her aside and lifted the novice to her feet. Looking into her face with a clear eye, she said, after a frightening silence:

"Could you be a Carmelite?"

"No!" panted the novice, and she drew back, as if she were at that moment about to be imprisoned behind the grille.

"If you cannot be a Carmelite, my child, you can be nothing."

"She'd be happy enough," intervened Patrick comfortably, "in an easier Order."

"She will be happy—we will all be happy—only in Heaven," said the Carmelite coldly. "Could you not even try to be a Carmelite?" asked the aged woman.

"No!" begged the novice. "I couldn't do it!"

"Why not?"

"To be always shut in?" trembled the girl.

"It is an enclosed Order," agreed the Superioress calmly.

"I couldn't stand it!"

"How do you know?" catechized the Superioress.

For answer the girl burst into such a sobbing wail that Patrick drew her to her broad bosom and turned on her aunt.

"Ye have no heart!" she upbraided. "Badgering the poor child! 'Tisn't that we expected from you! Don't heed her," she comforted Teresa. "My poor little girsha! Don't mind her. Sure we can't all be saints. You'll do your best. You can't do more."

"But," sobbed Teresa, "I want to be a saint. 'Tis to . . . to . . . to be a saint I joined the nuns." Her voice came out through her nose, miserably. "If I can't be a saint, I don't *want* to be a nun!"

The old woman comforted her, and finally restored her to a whimpering silence. Looking up, they saw they were alone. The grille was closed. The veil was hidden. The Superioress had gone.

The two pilgrims went back to their pension. That afternoon, without discussion, they went on to Saint Malo. There the novice was expected to find bodily rest, as at Lisieux she had been expected to find calm of soul.

IV

Saint Malo faces across a wide estuary the modern watering-place of Dinard. At night they saw the lights in the hotels, and cafés, and more colored lights beaded all around the roof of the casino; and sometimes they heard music across the still surface of the water. Steamers from Southampton and the Channel Islands floated in the bay at anchor. Patrick was charmed with her room in the convent where they stayed. It looked directly across at Dinard. She wrote to Mother Mary Mell that she had a "grandstand," and that she was thinking of going across in a rowboat some night to gamble in the Casino and make the fortune of the Order. Becoming serious in a postscript, she said that Teresa had not yet made up her mind, but that she was "behaving with the most edifying devotion."

Not only did the novice attend every service in the convent, but she had become pious beyond description, daily spending long hours alone in adoration in the chapel. But when Patrick noticed that she left her lunch untouched on her table on the third day of her arrival, and went up to the novice's cell to ask if this were wise, she made a frightening discovery. She found that the mattress and bedclothes had been rolled up

and put away under the bed, and all the girl's flannel under-
clothing was hanging in her cupboard. At once she went down
to the chapel, and hissed at the solitary worshipper to come
out, beckoning madly with her bony finger.

"Sister Teresa," she said severely, "you are refusing your food.
Is there any reason for this?"

The novice hung her head and said nothing.

"Answer me, Sister."

Still the novice kept her eyes on the parquet.

"I command you, Sister, to answer me."

"There is no reason," whispered the novice.

"Then eat up your food in future," ordered the nun. "Do
you want to make a skeleton out of yourself?" And she added
more easily, "Don't you know right well I'm supposed to bring
you home as plump as a duck?"

The novice raised two large, sad eyes.

"Sister Patrick," she begged, "I will obey if you command
me. But I want to do penance for my sins, and for the sins of
the world. I feel I have received a higher command."

"What higher command?" blustered the old woman, taken
aback. "What on earth are you talking about, Sister?"

Teresa sighed.

"The sins of the world are all about us," she smiled sadly.
"I see them every night from my window, across the water,
in the dens and gambling-houses. All lit up like the fires of Hell
to lure poor souls astray. I dreamed the first night I came
here that the Devil lives over there. I saw his red eyes in the
air. I saw that this convent was put here specially to atone for
the wickedness that surrounds it."

"Holy Mother!" cried the nun. "What are you talking
about, girl? Sister Teresa, let me tell you that if you ate a
proper supper . . . And by the same token, Miss, no wonder
you have dreams if you sleep on the laths of the bed. Do
you," she threatened, "sleep on the laths of the bed?"

The novice once more hung her head, and once more she
had to be bullied into replying.

"I do, Sister," she confessed unhappily.

"Well, then, let there be an end of it! What right have you to be going on with these andrewmartins off of your own bat? You know right well you must ask permission of your superior before you do the like. And that reminds me," she cried, grabbing the girl's flank, and then standing back from her in horror, with her gummy mouth open. "You haven't a stitch on you! Go upstairs at once, Miss, and dress yourself properly. I'll be after you in two minutes. I'm worn out and tormented with your vagaries! Ten times I told Mother Mary Mell . . ."

She pointed upstairs—a figure of Justice.

The novice went, tearful, head hanging. In two minutes the old nun followed. She opened the door of the cell. The girl lay on the ground, her arms stretched out like a crucifix, her dilated eyes fixed as on a vision over her head. The old nun entered the room, closed the door, and thundered:

"Get up out o' that!"

The novice did not move.

"Miss!" said the old woman, pale as a sheet, "how dare you disobey me!"

The novice trembled as if a wind had ruffled her spirit. With her heart battering inside in her, Patrick walked over and looked down. The big brown eyes, so strikingly dark in that pale pink-and-white face, stared up past her. Patrick looked up at the electric light bulb. She looked all about her. The thick-moted afternoon sun slanted in across the bed. A hissing suspiration below the window was followed by the little groan of the gravel dragging back under the wave. Then she saw a slimy brown insect, with wavering head, creep to the white ear of the novice, and she screamed:

"An earwig! Climbing into your ear!"

Teresa sat up as if she was stung. The fright passed. The two looked at each other with hate in their eyes. At the door, Patrick said:

"I'll wait in the garden."

In complete silence they walked four miles that afternoon. They did the same the following morning. That was their last full day. On the final afternoon Patrick spoke:

"We will be in Saint Anthony's to-morrow night. Do you know, yet, my dear, if you have a vocation?"

"I have decided to join the Carmelites," said the novice. They halted. They looked across the sea-wall into the blue of Dinard. A few lights were already springing up over there— the first dots in the long, golden necklet that already they had come to know so well. A lone sea-gull squawked over the glassy water. The sunset behind the blue pinnacles of the resort was russet.

"And what's wrong with our own Order, Sister dear?" asked Patrick of the vacancy before her.

"I feel, dear Sister Patrick," judged the novice, staring ahead of her, "that it is too worldly."

"How is it too worldly?" asked Patrick in a whisper.

"Well, dear Sister Patrick," pronounced the novice, "I see, for example, that you all eat too much."

The little wavelets fell almost inaudibly, drunken with the fullness of the tide, exhausted and soothed by their own completion.

"I shall tell Mother Mary Mell that you think so," whispered the old nun.

"There is no need, dear Sister. It will be my duty to tell her myself. I will pray for you all when I am in the Carmelites. I love you all. You are all kind and generous. But, dear Sister, I feel that very few nuns really have the right vocation to be nuns." Patrick closed her eyes tightly. The novice continued: "I will surrender myself to the divine Love. The death I desire is the death of Love. The death of the Cross."

They heard only the baby tongues of the waves. The evening star blazed in the russet sky. The old nun saw it, and she said, in part a statement, in part a prayer, in part a retort:

"Sweet Star of the Sea!"

Teresa raised her dark eyes to the star and she intoned in her girlish voice the poem of Saint Thérèse:

> *"Come, Mother, once again,*
> *Who camest first to chide.*
> *Come once again, but then*
> *To smile—at eventide."*

The old nun fiddled with her beads. She drew long breaths through her nose. She tried several times to speak. She gestured that they must go back. They turned and walked slowly back to the convent, side by side; the old nun as restless as if she were in bodily agony, the novice as sedate and calm as a statue. After a while Patrick fumbled in her pocket, and found a chocolate, and popped it into her mouth. Then she stopped chewing, and threw an eye at her companion. At the look of intense sorrow in the face beside her, she hunched up her shoulders and as silently as she could, she gulped the fragments whole.

On the journey homeward they did not speak one word to each other: all the way to Rouen in the trotting auto-rail; in the clanking train to Dieppe; on the boat; in the English train. In silence they arrived at Saint Anthony's, among the dank beechwoods, now softly dripping, in time to hear the first hoo-hoo of the owl, and to troop in with the rest of the community for evening chapel. Mother Mary Mell barely had time to ask the old nun how she had enjoyed her holiday— that first holiday in thirty-one years. Patrick's eyes fluttered. She recalled the lights of Dinard.

"It was lovely, Mother!"

Mary Mell caught the flicker of hesitation. Just as they crossed the tessellated threshold of the chapel, she whispered quickly, "And Teresa?"

Patrick, who had been waiting for that question ever since the final afternoon in Saint Malo, and yet had no answer ready, took refuge behind the chapel's interdiction of silence. She smiled reassuringly, nodded, smiled, nodded again, and then,

very solemn and pious, she walked in with her head down.
She said her prayers badly. She slept hardly at all that night.
She heard every crackling branch and fluttering night-bird. For
what, in the name of the Most High, was she to say to Mary
Mell? And what was she to say to the community in the
morning? As she tossed and tumbled, she thought of Teresa
sleeping peacefully in her cell, and the old woman burst into
tears of rage.

In the morning there was no Teresa. She had left the convent, through a ground-floor window, before anybody was
awake, and gone on the milk-train to London. She had walked
across the city at that hour when the sun emphasizes the
position of the East End, and the sleepers in the parks that she
traversed are unwrapping their newspaper blankets. A sister-
in-law coming out to collect the morning post found a nun
sitting on the doorstep. She had breakfast, in a tennis-frock,
along with the family.

She saw the convent only once again—about two years later
when she brought her husband to see it. As they got out of the
train she looked up into the familiar beeches at the steam of the
engine caught in the branches, and she remembered how
every train used to make the woods seem infinitely lonely
and the convent darker and more melancholy, because that
white steam suggested people traveling, and the luxury of the
world she had renounced. Her George, who was a Protestant,
and who was much excited by this expedition, nodded solemnly,
and began to get an uncomfortable feeling that he was married
to a nun. They were entertained politely. Old Sister Patrick
did not appear. As they left, the starting train again sent its
gushes of steam into the branches, and now those branches
again seemed to Teresa to clutch not only at the white smoke
but at her own heart. She felt that the woods enclosed a
refuge from the world of which she had, irrevocably, become
a part. As she snuggled down into her fur collar she gazed out of

her big eyes at her husband, and said, with a shake of her little head:

"Ah George! George! You will never know what I gave up to marry you!"

He smiled adoringly at her as, in obedience to a gesture, he leaned over to put a cigarette between her rouged lips.

"My precious Teresa," he murmured softly, and patted her knee.

She shook her head at him again, with a pitying smile.

"Has it upset you, my sweet?" he asked dismally.

Saying never a word, she kept gazing at him fixedly, as if he were a stranger. He huffed and hawed, and hedged himself behind his newspaper, looking as despondent as he considered proper. For as he explained to his colleagues in the morning, his wife was "a very spiritual woman" and on occasions like this she always made him feel that he had the soul of a hog.

THE CONFRONTATION

Georges Bernanos

Father Donissan didn't get in till very late. And long after his return, Father Menou-Segrais, with a book in his hand which he did not read, sat listening to his curate tramping up and down the room above.

"We shall have to thrash everything out soon," mused the old priest. He had always known an explanation would be necessary, but until then he had abstained from provoking it, too wise to deprive the young priest of the beneficial experience of having to make the first move. The last noises of the day had died down, except for those monotonous steps sounding through the thickness of the walls.

Father Menou-Segrais considered: "Why tonight, rather than tomorrow or any other time? The visit of Father Demange must have upset me in some way. . . ." Nevertheless the foreboding of some exceptional and inevitable event persisted beyond all reasoning, and his tension increased with every minute. Suddenly the passage door creaked, and somebody knocked twice. Father Donissan stood in the doorway.

"I was waiting for you, my boy," said Father Menou-Segrais simply.

"I know," answered the young man humbly. But he instantly drew himself up, looked straight into the dean's eyes and announced firmly, all in one breath:

"I feel I should ask the bishop to recall me to Tourcoing. Please help me in this, and don't hold back anything you know about me, don't spare me in any way—"

"Wait a minute—wait a minute," interrupted Father Menou-Segrais. "You say you feel you should. You *should*. Why should you?"

"Parochial work," he retorted, in the same manner, "is beyond me altogether. My superior thought so, and so do you, I know. In a place like this I do more harm than good. The lowest peasant in the parish would be ashamed of a priest like me, without experience or knowledge or real dignity. However hard I try, how can I hope to make up for it?"

"There's no need to go into all that," said the dean of Campagne. "I see what you mean. Your scruples may be justified. And for my part I'm prepared to ask monseigneur to recall you, but it still remains a very delicate matter. We really didn't ask a great deal of you here. And yet it was too much, you say?"

Father Donissan bent his head.

"Don't be a baby!" exclaimed the dean. "I am going to appear hard to you, but I am obliged to be. The diocese cannot afford to feed one useless mouth, my boy."

"I—I can see that all right," stammered the young priest. "Actually—I don't know yet—I thought perhaps—in a monastery I might find something temporary, anyhow. . . ."

"A monastery! Your kind, young man, have that word forever on their lips! Monks are the chosen men of the church, sir—her reserve. A monastery, indeed! As though it were some kind of sanatorium or hospital!"

"I know—" Father Donissan tried to say, but a confused stutter was all that could be heard. His scarlet cheeks quivered, but even his extreme emotion did not drain the blood from them. This was the only outward sign of his infinite distress. Even his voice became steady again as he asked:

"Well then—what am I wanted for?"

"That," answered the dean of Campagne, "is the first sensible word you have spoken. Since you admit that you are incapable of guiding others, how can you be relied on to know what is best for you yourself? God and your bishop, my boy, have seen to it that you shall be directed—by me."

"I agree," he answered, after a moment's imperceptible hesitation, "yet I beg you to—"

The dean cut him short with an imperious gesture, and he stared with frightened inquisitiveness at the old priest, so courteous as a rule, suddenly become rigid and imperturbable, with eyes like flint.

"It's a serious business. Your superiors let you take Holy Orders: I can't believe they came to such a decision lightly. On the other hand, this incapacity to which you referred just now—"

"Let me explain," interrupted the unhappy young man, in the same colorless voice. "Surely, there's some kind of work I can do for God, that wouldn't be quite beyond my scope. My health is very good, anyhow—" He broke off, ashamed, in his sublime innocence of opposing such a feeble argument to so much eloquent reasoning.

"Health is a gift of God," answered Father Menou-Segrais, solemnly. "Alas, I know what it's worth better than you do. Your share of physical strength, your aptitude for certain kinds of manual labor, were perhaps indications of some lesser vocation to which Providence summoned you. Is it ever too late to recognize an involuntary error, with the help of reliable outside opinion? Should you really try again, or would it be preferable to—to—"

"To—what?" ventured Father Donissan.

"To get back to your cow's tail," concluded the dean drily. "Mind: I am merely considering the alternatives, I am not suggesting a solution for the moment. Thank God, you're not one of those hypersensitive lads who freeze up at a harsh word and get no good from it. You're not likely to lose your head. And for my part I have done my duty, though with apparent cruelty."

"Thank you," said the young priest gently. His voice had grown strangely firm. "At the very beginning of our talk, God gave me the strength to hear some very hard facts from your lips. Why should He not help me until the end? Please answer that question yourself. Why should I wait any longer?"

"Well, you see—" muttered Father Menou-Segrais, taken

off his guard, "I'd prefer to think it over for a few weeks—
and give you a chance to—"

"What's the use? If I'm not to judge my own case, and I
certainly don't feel I can. I want your opinion—the sooner
the better."

"You may be ready enough to hear it, my boy, but hardly,
I should think, to follow it unquestioningly," said the dean
with forced brutality. "In such a case to provoke what frightens
you is a sign of weakness rather than courage."

"I know, I know—you're quite right," cried Father Donissan, "you can see into my heart. But I appeal to your charity,
Father—have mercy on me, let me know the worst. After that,
I feel I shall have the strength—I know I shall. God always
helps the fallen to rise again."

Father Menou-Segrais scrutinized him sharply.

"Can you be so sure that my mind is made up," he said,
"that I have no doubts?"

Father Donissan shook his head.

"It doesn't take long to size up a man like me," he said.
"You're only trying to let me down lightly. At least, give me
credit—before God—of absolute obedience. Tell me what you
want me to do, don't leave me in this uncertainty!"

"You are right," said the dean after a pause. "I'm bound to
say you are right. Your intentions are good, at times they seem
even to be enlightened. I understand your eagerness to master
yourself once and for all. But the verdict you are expecting
me to pronounce may be a temptation beyond your powers.
You want to know it—very well. But will you be able to carry
it out?"

"I think so," answered the young priest in a muffled voice.
"Besides, shall I ever be better prepared than I am tonight,
to receive my cross and bear it? Believe me, Father, the time
has come. I'm only a clumsy, ignorant priest incapable of
inspiring affection. As a little boy I was a very poor scholar,
and as I grew up—well, I just got on everybody's nerves. By
some miracle of charity Father Demange got me ordained.

. . . I'd no understanding, no memory, I wasn't even persevering . . . and yet . . ."

He hesitated, but the dean signed to him to go on.

"And yet," he continued with difficulty, "I've never been able to get over a kind of obstinacy. The scorn I so well deserve rouses in me such bitter, such violent resentment that I should never be able to overcome it in an ordinary way—"

He broke off, as though terrified of having said too much. The dean's small eyes stared penetratingly into his. He plunged, desperately: "Please don't put me off. Now's the time. Tonight, really. . . . You can't imagine how I—"

Father Menou-Segrais rose abruptly from his chair and walked towards the window, leaning on his stick as though deeply absorbed. Then suddenly he straightened his back and said:

"I am deeply moved, my child, by your submission. I must have appeared very brutal and I am going to be brutal again. It would be quite easy for me to evade the issue in a number of ways. But I'd rather be straight with you. You have just put yourself into my hands. . . . Do you happen to know whose hands?"

"Please—don't—" murmured the young man, his voice trembling.

"I will tell you: You have put yourself into the hands of *a man you do not respect.*"

Father Donissan became livid.

"Whom you do not respect," insisted Father Menou-Segrais. "The life I lead here could well be that of any well-to-do layman. You might as well admit it; you are ashamed of me and my semi-idleness. My experience, which fools consider so important, is worthless in your eyes, and barren. There are many other points I might mention, but that will suffice. My child, in such a grave issue little considerations of courtesy and tact must go to the wall. Tell me, am I right?"

At the first words of this strange confession Father Donissan had dared to raise his eyes in stupefaction, and he did not lower them again.

"You must answer me," Father Menou-Segrais went on. "You must obey me in this before I can come to any decision about you. You have the right to challenge my way of life. I can be your judge in this matter, but I will not be your tempter. Simply answer: 'Yes' or 'No.'"

"The answer is 'Yes,'" said Father Donissan quietly. "But the test is almost beyond me—please don't prolong it."

Tears started in his eyes, and the dean was scarcely able to catch his last words, spoken almost in a whisper.

Already the unhappy boy was filled with devouring self-reproach, for his timid appeal for mercy now seemed mere weakness. After a short inner conflict he went on:

"I have obeyed you, and now no doubt I should hold my tongue and wait, but—but I can't. God doesn't want me to let you imagine. . . . Honestly, that is only an opinion, an involuntary impression. . . . I'm not saying this is self-defense," he added more steadily, "you can see for yourself how evil I am: Providence has stripped me. And now—now—"

His hands clutched the air for support, and he threw out his long arms. Then his knees gave way and he fell forward on his face.

"My dear child!" cried Father Menou-Segrais, in an agonized voice.

He dragged the unconscious body to the divan and with a huge effort hoisted it up. The bony face showed white against the red leather cushions.

"Come—come—" muttered the old dean, struggling to unbutton the cassock with stiff arthritic fingers; but the threadbare material was the first to give way, revealing a coarse bloodstained shirt.

Then the broad, deep chest rose and fell, restored to its natural rhythm. Roughly, the dean thrust open his shirt. "I thought as much," he said with a twisted smile.

From the armpits to the loins the young man was imprisoned in a rigid sheath of stiffest horsehair, coarsely woven; the narrow thong which held this horrible garment in place was so tightly knotted that Father Menou-Segrais had great difficulty in untying it. The skin revealed was burnt, as if by caustic, by the intolerable friction of the horsehair, in places it had been entirely rubbed away, in others it rose in blisters as broad as a hand-stretch which gave it the appearance of one vast sore oozing water and blood. The foul grayish-brown bristle was soaked in it.

From a deeper wound in the side—inadequately bound with a rag of hemp—bright red blood was flowing, drop by drop. Father Menou-Segrais removed the obstacle and hastily withdrew his reddened fingers.

The curate opened his eyes. They searched each corner of the room without recognizing it, and returned to the familiar face of the dean, at first with increasing astonishment. Suddenly he saw his cassock, torn open, and his blood-stained shirt. He fell back swiftly and covered his face with his hands.

But Father Menou-Segrais with a gentle, almost maternal gesture was already drawing them away from the rugged features.

"My child," he breathed, with indefinable emphasis, "Our Lord is not displeased with you."

But he instantly resumed his usual tone of somewhat condescending benevolence with which he chose to mask his feelings.

"You'll put that infernal contraption in the fire, my boy, first thing tomorrow morning. You must find something better than that. God preserve me from talking mere common sense to you. In good, as in evil, one should always be a little mad. But I consider your attempts at mortification rather indiscreet. A respectable young priest keeps his underwear spotless. Get up, now," continued this strange old man, "and draw a little nearer to me. Our talk isn't ended yet, though we've got the worst over. Come and sit down over here—come on now, I'm holding you."

He installed the young man in his own armchair and went on talking as he casually slipped a cushion under the aching head. Then he sat down on a low chair, and drew his rug about him with a shiver; he stared thoughtfully into the fire, and the flames danced in his keen bold eyes. At last he said:

"Your opinion of me, child, is more or less correct, but you're mistaken in one particular. I judge myself far more severely than you imagine. I am almost in port, and my hands are empty. . . ." He quietly poked the flaming logs. "You're a different sort of man altogether, and you've turned me inside out like a glove. When I asked monseigneur to send you, I had a rather foolish notion of taking under my wing a—well, a 'blacklisted' young curate without any of those natural gifts for which I have so great a weakness, and I fancied I would shape him, to the best of my ability, into a nice parish priest. God knows it would have been a heavy enough burden, at the very end of my life! But I was too pleased with my seclusion to finish dying in peace. The judgment of God, dear child, should overtake us in the middle of our task—the judgment of God!

"It is you"—he whispered, after a long pause—"who are shaping me."

Father Donissan did not even avert his face at these amazing words. His wide-open eyes showed no astonishment, but from his moving lips the dean saw that he was praying.

"They were not able to recognize the rarest gifts of the Spirit," the dean went on. "They never see anything! It is God who names us. The names we wear are only borrowed names. My child, the Spirit of Our Lord is within you."

Three strokes of the first Angelus sounded outside like a solemn warning, but they did not hear it. The logs crumbled softly, into ashes.

"And now," continued Father Menou-Segrais, "now—I need you. There is no other priest, even had he seen as clearly into your heart as I have, who would have dared to speak as I have done tonight. But I had to. We are at the turning point in life, which comes to each one of us, when the truth forces itself irresistibly upon us, when each of us need only hold out his arms to be swept straight up to the surface of darkness and into the sunshine of God. At such a time human caution is a trap for fools. Holiness!" cried the old man in a deep voice. "As I pronounce that word in your presence, for you alone, I know what it is that I inflict on you. Do you realize what it means: a vocation, a call! There, where God awaits you, you will have to go, up and up, or lose yourself forever. Do not expect men to help you. I am fully aware of the responsibility I have taken, but I felt justified in speaking to you like this after a final proof of your obedience and simplicity. By mistrusting not merely your own power but what God intends for you, you were heading into a blind alley. At my own risk and peril I have set you back onto your road, I am giving you back to the hungry souls who will feed on you. May the blessing of Our Lord be with you, my child!"

At those last words, like a soldier who knows he has been wounded and raises himself instinctively before falling back, Father Donissan stood up. His face was motionless, tight-lipped, with heavy jaws and obstinate brow. Only the pale eyes betrayed agonized hesitation. For a while he stared restlessly round the room. Then he caught sight of the cross, hanging on the wall, and looked quickly back at the old man: all the light in his eyes seemed to have been put out. The dean could read in them only blind submission, to which the tragic disorder of his soul, still uplifted by terror, lent a sublime dignity.

"Do you mind if I go?" he asked very simply, his voice still unsteady. "Just now, as I was listening to you, I thought I was done for, I felt so hopeless, but that's all over. . . . I—I think —I am—what you want me to be—and—and God won't let me be tried beyond my strength."

He immediately left the room, and for the first time the door closed noiselessly behind him.

STORIES ON THE VERANDAH

Brian Friel

There was not a more popular patient in the County Donegal Hospital for Tuberculosis than Maurice Barry—Barry, as everyone called him, as if that were his Christian name. He was a gay, pleasant fellow, always ready for a joke. To look at him, one would never have thought he was nearing fifty, not that he wore well (he was going bald and had false teeth, but the hair was cunningly arranged and he removed the false teeth only after lights-out), but he was a bachelor and had about him the freshness of a much younger man. The two men who shared the ward with him, Porter and Field, were ten years younger than he but they were both married and settled and although they were good sports too—Porter especially—they had none of Barry's dash and exuberance. He was a teacher and could talk to the doctors with easy familiarity about chess and bridge and books and golf (he was secretary to his own club); he was a special favorite of the chaplain because he had a brother who was a missionary in the Philippine Islands; he delighted the nurses with his harmless flirting and his just-so-daring jokes that sent them squealing with pretended shock; and he said things to Miss Pindle, the Matron, that no man had ever said to her before and in spite of herself she had to smile. But then there was never any danger of Barry going beyond the accepted limits; he was too gentlemanly for that. Neither Porter nor Field could have taken any of those liberties, Field because he was a quiet, reserved man anyhow, and Porter because he had a reputation for doubtful stories and the women were cautious with him.

"Pay no attention to him," Barry would say to the nurses. "He's just a soured old married man. Now you girls should concentrate on me instead, free as the wind and just dying for a wife. Come on. Who'll have me? Any takers?"

"Go on, Barry! Go on!" they would say. "Many a poor girl heard that from you! You're not going to break any more hearts, not in here anyway!"

"Listen to them!" Barry would call across to his two friends. "Me break anybody's heart? Boys, tell them the truth. Go ahead and tell them how desperate I am. As true as God, girls, no one will take me. I'm practically at my wits' end."

"Not from what we have heard," they would say. "If some of the stories we have heard are only half true, you have a lot to answer for, you villain you!"

"Now you listen to me and I'll tell you something I've never told anyone in my whole life: the only woman I ever kissed was my mother. Cross my heart! Strike me dead if I'm telling a lie!"

And so they would go on and on and on, pleasantly, innocuously, killing time, keeping things harmonious, preventing the jealousies and depressions that destroyed the spirit in other wards.

Occasionally Porter would try to join in with some exaggerated story about his past when he was laying telephone lines in Armagh or Tyrone, but the nurses were wary of him and he usually kept his best recollections for nighttime when they were alone and the three of them would swap yarns for hours at a stretch. Porter's stories were rough but he told them directly and without artifice and they did not seem crude. Only when he began to talk about his wife did Barry become embarrassed and he would call to Field, "Terrible man this, isn't he? I don't believe a word of it, not one word. Do you?" To which Field replied, as he did to so many questions, "That's the way. That's the way."

Wednesday was visiting day. Barry was visited every week without fail by two maiden aunts, Aunt Minnie and Aunt Etta, with whom he lived. They were very old ladies, very small and very frail. The journey from the town out to the hospital was as much as they were fit for and when they came into the ward, they touched the tips of his fingers and asked him how he was feeling and then sat down and waited for strength to gather in them again to make the journey home. Barry and they never had much to talk about after he had inquired about Uncle Joe who was bedridden and could not come but who sent his best wishes. So the aunts just sat there, their heads shaking in unison, blinking at their dead sister's child.

Porter's wife came most weeks. She was a young, strong woman with a challenging look. They had no family. From the moment she arrived, Porter spoke softly to her in a monotone and every so often she would toss her head back and fill the room with her rich laugh. At that the aunts would stop nodding. They would look over their shoulders at Porter's bed and their pale mouths would pucker quizzically. Such a jolly man, their faces said; such a jolly couple.

"Easy there, Porter! Easy!" Barry would call over the heads of Aunt Minnie and Aunt Etta. "There's a time and a place for everything." He welcomed anything that distracted the aunts' faded eyes.

"Shut up!" Porter would call back brusquely.

"A bad lot, that man of yours, Mrs. Porter. I don't know why you ever married him. And I'll tell you something: he has Matron's old heart in a flutter; she can't drag herself away from him."

"Tell her from me that she can have him if she wants him," Mrs. Porter would call back. She had a habit of raising her voice encouragingly at the end of a sentence.

Very often Barry would call across to them throughout most of the visiting hour until Porter would get genuinely annoyed and tell him to bloody well entertain his own visitors.

Field's wife came every second week. It was difficult for her because she had eight young children and she had to bring them with her everywhere she went. They waited outside the building because of hospital regulations. She was a small, weary woman who spoke little. She just sat at the foot of his bed and studied everybody and everything in the ward: Barry, his aunts,

Porter, his wife, the paint on the walls, the lights, the floor, the bedclothes, the lockers. Most of the time Field looked out through the window at his family. Sometimes he would turn round to ask his wife a question about a bandage or spectacles or new shoes and she would answer lethargically in a word or two. But for the greater part of the hour he looked out at them, never waving or signaling messages or tapping at them, but staring evenly out at them. When the bell would ring, Mrs. Field would say, "Time up already? Well cheerio," and Field would reply, "Time up. That's the way," and Mrs. Field would take one long, last summarizing look around the ward and go off by herself, not waiting for Mrs. Porter, not recognizing the other patients beyond nodding to them. Then Mrs. Porter would rise, straighten her shoulders, say to her husband, "Be good. See you next week—maybe," call across to Barry, "Keep your eye on Matron for me!" to which Barry would have a quick comeback, and she would swagger off after wagging her fingers in a general farewell. The aunts were always the last to leave, reluctant to begin tapping their restored strength again. They usually waited until the ward orderly came to the door and clapped his hands. Then they would rise, kiss their nephew on the forehead, say, "We'll be back next week, Maurice; see you next week, Maurice," and shuffle down the passage, arm in arm. They stopped again at the door and waved back, and Barry would call, "Thanks again. Love to Uncle Joe. Good-by. Good-by."

For minutes after the visitors had gone, the ward would be silent, Porter and Field fingering their parcels of fruit and laundry, pretending to examine them, Barry waiting impatiently for them to forget the interruption in their routine. It was always he who initiated a conversation, who recreated the old, breezy mood.

"The way you whisper to that woman of yours, Porter! Have you no consideration for a man like me, a young single fellow?" Porter would either curse him concisely or not answer him at all. He would then turn to Field.

"And how are all the young Fields looking, eh? How many

have you? A dozen? Sixteen? No, no. Don't say a word; no
excuses. You quiet types are all the same. I've met your sort
before."

"There are only eight, Barry."

"*Only* eight! Do you hear that, Porter? *Only*, he says. Lord
you married men are all the same. It's boys like you, Field, who
ruin the chances of chaps like me. *Only* eight. No wonder the
women are afraid of us!"

He could keep this up for a quarter of an hour without
stopping, without encouragement, and if, after that time, the
other two were still preoccupied, there was always the diversion
of tea being brought in and he would start bantering with the
nurse and lay elaborate plans for a make-believe date with her
in the extern department. After tea Porter and Field would be
back to normal and by nighttime the visitors were completely
forgotten.

All three were due for discharge at the end of September
and as the time drew near they spent more and more time out
of bed, moving slowly around their own and neighboring wards
in dressing gown and slippers. Porter marked off the days on a
calendar which he kept under his pillow. Each morning he
took it out, announced the new date to the others, cursed the
old day to the depths of hell, and crossed it off with a
laborious X. He began composing a rhyme, of the type school-
boys use, which began, "This time—days, where shall we be?
Outside these gates to liberty." Then followed a catalogue of
the pleasures he had planned for himself, most of them having
to do with drinking and gambling. But since he had to list
these pleasures rhythmically, he sought the help of the other
two and together they spent hours at the job.

Porter's delight at getting home was so infectious that Field,
who never discussed his private life, now began to drop occasional bits of information. Barry and Porter learned only in
the last week that one of his children was a violinist and had
recently been selected for the Municipal Youth Orchestra, that
another was captain of the school football team, and that a

third was color-blind. Field mentioned this last as if it were a valuable and enviable qualification and in the warmth and simplicity of his telling, it appeared to Porter and Barry that indeed it was. He even mentioned Mrs. Field, referring to her casually as "she": "She thinks we should try to educate them all," or "She wouldn't have a picture on the walls if you were to go down on your knees before her." Though he tried to sound indifferent, he could never disguise completely the love he had for her. And once, when Porter in his careless, blustering way made some indelicate remark about Field's married life, Field flew into a rage and would have attacked him if Barry had not intervened and by his endless talking brought about a reconciliation between them.

They had their final X rays in the second week in September and the date of their discharge was fixed for the following Thursday. From the Monday of that week Barry was discontented and unsettled. Now Porter's rough speech began to irritate him and Field's reserve appeared secretive and sneaky. Before this they used to settle for the night about 5:00 P.M., listen to the radio perhaps, or yarn, or play a game of poker. But now that they had their all-clear the nurses were not so strict and allowed them to sit out on the verandah long after darkness had enveloped them.

It was on their second-last night together that Barry's irritation turned to uneasiness and then to anxiety. Instead of going inside as they had always done, the other two seemed to prefer to sit out there in the dark, not talking, just sitting smoking. He did his best to shift them but they were in no mood for cards or the radio, they said; they preferred to sit in the dark even though it had turned cold and there was a light dew. Then Porter began to say something about how strange life was and as soon as he spoke, Barry recognized the nameless anxiety that was disturbing him: it was the intimacy and confidence in Porter's behavior, something altogether new to their relationship. Barry paid no attention to what Porter was saying but became suddenly wary of the dark and the silence and the strange quietness in Porter's voice. Confidences were exchanged at a time like this, secrets revealed, and he wanted no confidences and no secrets. He took action before Porter's mood established itself. He broke in with a wild, hilarious tale of a girl from a country area where he once taught who went to London when she was eighteen and returned to her astonished parents within three weeks, bringing with her an Armenian husband who had one arm and a beard a yard long. The maneuver was a success. Field laughed until the smoke of his cigarette choked him and Porter and Barry added to the story a hundred indelicate and improbable conclusions. When they had hammered all the fun they could out of the incident, they went inside and listened to the radio.

On their last day he was almost convinced they conspired against him. They sat out in the sun all afternoon and watched it fall and saw the shadows lengthening around them. Barry flitted about, now joining them on the verandah, now going back into the ward to fiddle at the radio or to add another line to the letter he was writing. He could settle to nothing. Dusk came and after that darkness and still they sat out there, exchanging an occasional word, smoking, humming. Barry was disappointed in them, as disappointed as he used to be when he was at boarding school and Aunt Minnie and Aunt Etta did not turn up to visit him on a Saturday. He remembered all the plans they had made months ago to celebrate their last night in hospital: three crates of beer, whiskey, poker all night, maybe even a couple of the nurses in for a bit of a dance. They had let him down—Porter more than Field because it was he, he remembered, who had suggested the dancing, and now all he could do was sit out there on a hard seat, for all the world like a damn dummy, and kill himself smoking. Damn them and the hospital and whole bloody outfit! Tomorrow could not come a second soon enough!

He fidgeted around his bed for an hour longer than he needed but at last he had to join them: he needed their company too much. When he went out to them, they were not talking but sitting as if they were waiting for something. He dropped into the third chair and lit a cigarette. There was still warmth in the air but it had turned clammy. He put his handkerchief up to his mouth and removed his false teeth with the ease of a conjurer.

"Well, boys back to the big, bad world tomorrow. Any objections?"

No one answered him.

"Which reminds me, Porter. I always intended giving you this bit of advice on our last night together and I'm not going to shirk my duty. And the advice is this: if your work ever brings you into my county, I'm warning you, Porter, I'll have every married man alerted and as soon as you set foot in it, we'll run you out and keep you running until you drop with fatigue. I'm telling you now; the advice of a friend. Right, Field?"

Porter chuckled politely, tolerantly.

"Wouldn't I be justified, Field? Would you not do the same to protect the womenfolk of Monaghan? It's my duty, isn't it? No need to spare a man's feelings or anything like that. We're all men together, aren't we?"

"That's the way," said Field. "That's the way."

The silence became physical. Barry could feel it encompassing him, tightening on him. Along the road beyond the hospital walls cars raced by, full of gay, carefree people on their way to films and parties and concerts.

Then Porter began to speak. Without introduction, as if everything had been planned beforehand and he were just waiting for conditions to be right before he would begin, he began telling them the story of his life. His voice was soft and natural and although neither of the other two could see him, they knew his face was there before them, suspended in the blackness. No one stopped him or questioned him and he talked on and on without interruption. He did not tell them everything, they knew that; there were gaps in his story, details left out that some unsuspected delicacy in him prevented him from telling. Yet the narrative was heightened by this new reticence they never knew he had.

He was illegitimate, he told them. He had been reared in an orphanage run by nuns and had run away to sea when he was sixteen. He joined the British Army at the outbreak of war and was a prisoner in Italy for three years. He told them too about an Italian girl called Maria whom he had never mentioned in his previous boastings. But at that point in Porter's biography, Barry found himself not listening to the tale but listening to Porter telling the tale in this new, subdued, reminiscing voice. He had to stop this, to break it. When Porter was describing the girl's hands, Barry said, "For God's sake, Porter, who do you think you're fooling! You studying a girl's hands! Do you believe that, Field?"

The strange thing was that Porter made no reply but went on telling his story as if there had been no interruption. Now Barry stopped listening altogether. They're like drunk men, he thought, talking phony talk confidentially! Damn them anyway! But despite himself he heard Porter's more recent history, right up to his admitted longing for a family and heard Field's words of consolation and advice. Damn the pair of them! Damn the pair of them to blazes!

When Porter had done, there was silence again, a natural hiatus. It was cold now but neither Porter nor Field appeared to notice. Although Barry's feet were numb, sweat had broken out on his forehead. His body ached for movement, for action. "What about a bottle, boys, eh? Who's game to slip down to the gate lodge and get old Jacob to nip out for a bottle? I'll go myself. What'll it be, boys? Whiskey? Rum? Beer? Speak up and let the waiter hear the orders."

"Nothing for me, thanks, Barry," said Porter. "When I've waited this long, I can wait until tomorrow."

"You and I then, Field. We'll drink to the future of Casanova here. What will you have?"

"I don't feel like anything just now," said Field. "By the way, have you had a couple already? You're talking kind of . . . kind of lispy."

Barry slipped his teeth back into his mouth. "Like hell I have! You two are half shot yourselves, sitting out here in the bloody dark!" His voice turned to pleading. "Boys, why don't you come inside? Please."

Again they did not answer and once more the dark crept back in on them. Yet he could not leave them.

The game was only beginning: Field had to bare his damn soul too. He waited until Porter's story had subsided. When he began, Barry deliberately thought of other things. While Field's low voice droned on, he took out his teeth, closed his eyes and concentrated on his aunts and his uncle and his school and the other teachers and his brother working himself to death in those foreign islands and his brief, weary letters asking for prayers. But those thoughts irked him and he had to tune in to Field. His story was about his children and their sicknesses and their ambitions and their lessons and there was something about his wife's mother who was fond of a drop of gin and who upset his wife very badly when she went on one of her binges. All the time that Field talked, Porter listened intently, like a priest or a family doctor; Barry could feel him listening. The stupid, stupid fool, he thought; what the hell has got into them anyhow!

Then they waited for him to begin. No one said, "Your turn, Barry," but he knew, he knew, he knew. Two had spoken and it was the turn of the third. He trembled. His story. He dug his fingers into his knees and opened his mouth and closed his eyes and moved his face slowly over and back against the consoling darkness. His story . . . where to begin . . . what to tell. . . .

"You live with the aunts, Barry? The aunts and the uncle?" It was Porter who spoke.

"Yes."

"I suppose . . ." Porter hesitated, "I suppose that with them rearing you and all and you growing up and sort of looking

after them, I suppose you never got around to setting up a
place of your own?"

Panic was rising in him. Can I, he thought? Can I? Can I?

"It's awkward, I know," Porter went on. "I knew a chap in
Dungannon who was caught like that too. Decent sort he was.
But caught, like yourself." Porter had the whole night before
him. He was prepared to discuss the situation calmly, sym-
pathetically, helpfully. "You play a lot of golf and that stuff,
don't you? I mean you must meet a lot of suitable women out
there on the links."

"Yes," said Barry. Now, he said to himself. Now. Now.

"But what I mean is," said Porter, "there must be some
times in your life, man, when all this gadding about gets you
down, when you wish to God you hadn't flirted so much and
had settled down like the rest of us. Am I not right?"

"Yes." Now. Before the second passes. Now.

"Sure I know. I know. A bit of fun in your youth—there's
nothing like it. But when you get to our time of day, I mean
that's a different story. . . ."

Suddenly the verandah was flooded with light: someone
inside had switched it on. His false teeth! He whipped them
out, slipped them into his mouth, and managed a grin at
Porter and Field. They had not noticed.

"That's an improvement," said Porter calmly, looking up at
the naked bulb. "But as I was saying, Barry." He crossed his
legs and lit a cigarette.

The spell was broken, the moment gone. It was too late
now.

"Real good, isn't he?" said Barry quickly. "Do you know,
Porter, you could run a terrific lonely-hearts column—you
sound so damned sincere, straight from the bleeding heart."

Porter waited until he had finished and then went patiently
on. "And then there's your job with good pay and a good
pension. Not every man has that to offer a woman. And I can
tell you this: nothing appeals to them more than a pension.
Now if you only looked around in the right places, there's

bound to be a woman who would take you for the pension itself."

"Millions of them! I have an Alsatian at home to keep them at bay!"

"But seriously, Barry. If I was you, I wouldn't give up hope. There you are, man, only just past your prime and sweet damn all to show for it. It's a sheer waste, isn't it, Field?"

"You're right there," said Field. "That's what it is."

"So what I think you need, Barry, is just a wee bit more self-confidence. Get out there, man, and look about you. And don't be disheartened if the first few turn you down. Just you keep on trying."

Barry sprang to his feet. He was sweating and trembling. His eyes were filled with tears. Had he been a different man, he would have flung himself on top of Porter and flailed him with his fists. But violence had never been part of his life. His strongest reaction was a half roar, half cry.

"Shut up, you bastard you! Shut up, will you! Shut up and leave me alone!"

He staggered back into the ward, flung himself into bed and lay sobbing under the bedclothes.

"God!" breathed Porter after he had gone. "What did I say? What did I do wrong?"

"Don't ask me," said Field.

"Did I say something wrong? Do you think I said something hurtful?"

"Not that I heard," Field replied.

"I was only trying to help. I didn't mean no harm."

"That's the way. That's the way."

"Boy. What a roar he let out of him! Maybe I should go in and explain to him?"

"Explain what?"

"I don't know . . . that I wasn't being nosy . . . that I didn't mean no harm."

"I wouldn't if I was you."

"But he's in there crying like a baby. Listen to him."

"Let him be. Tomorrow he'll have forgotten all about it."

"But I said nothing," said Porter, trying to remember what it was he had said. "At least I don't think I said . . ."

"Forget it," said Field. "That's the way some people are. Like him there. Touchy. Forget it."

"Touchy," Porter repeated.

"It will be all forgotten in the morning," said Field. "As if nothing had happened."

"I suppose you're right," said Porter, sighing. "As if nothing had happened. It will be all forgotten."

"Wait and see. All over and done with."

"He's touchy, that's what it is," said Porter. "A touchy guy."

"That's the way," said Field. "Forget it. Forget it."

The aunts arrived at nine the following morning while the three men were still packing. The old ladies were ecstatic with joy and Aunt Minnie tiptoed across to Field and whispered to him that they had an extra surprise for their nephew: Uncle Joe was outside in the taxi! Of course he shouldn't have come really—their doctor would be furious—but there he was! Barry too was at the top of his form. He hugged the nurses in farewell and kissed the Matron and the women all squealed with delight.

"Take him away, Miss Barry! Take him away!" Matron called roguishly. "And when you get him home, put him across your knee and give him a good spanking. He's become terribly bold since he came here!"

There was a lot of laughing and a lot of talk and Barry excelled himself with witty remarks. Then, as if the previous night had never taken place, he went over to Field and shook his hand and told him to be kinder to the census collector in the future. He then went across to Porter.

"Good-by, Porter," he said breezily. "Remember all the advice I gave you. See you around some time."

Porter took his outstretched hand. "Good-by, Maurice," he said.

"Maurice?" Barry exclaimed, turning and pretending to

search around the room. The nurses laughed and clapped their hands. "Oh, you mean me? Come off it, Porter! No need for those refinements just because the ladies are here. You forget that we all know you too well!"

After more handshakings and more farewells, Barry and the aunts got the length of the car where Uncle Joe sat grinning. Barry hopped into the front, gave the others a last wave, called, "Home, James," to the driver for all to hear. The car moved off. As it passed out the gate, they met Mrs. Field surrounded by her eight children and followed by her mother who looked to be very merry and very unsteady; and further up the road they passed Mrs. Porter wearing a dazzling scarlet frock and a mad yellow hat.

"Now," said Barry, turning from the window, smiling radiantly at the aunts. "Bring me up to date on all the news of the outside world. I've been out of circulation too long." And while they both were telling him about their cat being sick yesterday and about Mrs. Doyle next door losing her purse on the bus and about the breadman being knocked down by a bicycle, he heard only snatches of what they said because a loneliness that was close to despair had settled on him, he knew, forever.

SAINT JOAN

George Bernard Shaw

Joan, chained by the ankles, is brought in through the arched door behind the prisoner's stool by a guard of English soldiers. With them is the Executioner and his assistants. They lead her to the prisoner's stool, and place themselves behind it after taking off her chain. She wears a page's black suit. Her long imprisonment and the strain of the examinations which have preceded the trial have left their mark on her; but her vitality still holds; she confronts the court unabashed, without a trace of the awe which their formal solemnity seems to require for the complete success of its impressiveness.

— THE INQUISITOR. [*kindly*] Sit down, Joan. [*She sits on the prisoner's stool*] You look very pale today. Are you not well?
— JOAN.   Thank you kindly: I am well enough. But the Bishop sent me some carp; and it made me ill.
— CAUCHON.   I am sorry. I told them to see that it was fresh.
— JOAN.   You meant to be good to me, I know; but it is a fish that does not agree with me. The English thought you were trying to poison me.
— CAUCHON.   What!
                          } [*together*] {
— THE CHAPLAIN.   No, my lord.
— JOAN. [*continuing*] They are determined that I shall be burnt as a witch; and they sent their doctor to cure me; but he was forbidden to bleed me because the silly people believe that a witch's witchery leaves her if she is bled; so he only called me filthy names. Why do you leave me in the hands of the English? I should be in the hands of the Church. And why must I be chained by the feet to a log of wood? Are you afraid I will fly away?

—D'ESTIVET. [*harshly*] Woman: it is not for you to question the court: it is for us to question you.

—COURCELLES. When you were left unchained, did you not try to escape by jumping from a tower sixty feet high? If you cannot fly like a witch, how is it that you are still alive?

—JOAN. I suppose because the tower was not so high then. It has grown higher every day since you began asking me questions about it.

—D'ESTIVET. Why did you jump from the tower?

—JOAN. How do you know that I jumped?

—D'ESTIVET. You were found lying in the moat. Why did you leave the tower?

—JOAN. Why would anybody leave a prison if they could get out?

—D'ESTIVET. You tried to escape?

—JOAN. Of course I did; and not for the first time either. If you leave the door of the cage open the bird will fly out.

—D'ESTIVET. [*rising*] That is a confession of heresy. I call the attention of the court to it.

—JOAN. Heresy, he calls it! Am I a heretic because I try to escape from prison?

—D'ESTIVET. Assuredly, if you are in the hands of the Church, and you wilfully take yourself out of its hands, you are deserting the Church; and that is heresy.

—JOAN. It is great nonsense. Nobody could be such a fool as to think that.

—D'ESTIVET. You hear, my lord, how I am reviled in the execution of my duty by this woman. [*He sits down indignantly*]

—CAUCHON. I have warned you before, Joan, that you are doing yourself no good by these pert answers.

—JOAN. But you will not talk sense to me. I am reasonable if you will be reasonable.

—THE INQUISITOR. [*interposing*] This is not yet in order. You forget, Master Promoter, that the proceedings have not been formally opened. The time for questions is after she has sworn on the Gospels to tell us the whole truth.

—JOAN. You say this to me every time. I have said again and again that I will tell you all that concerns this trial. But I cannot tell you the whole truth: God does not allow the whole truth to be told. You do not understand it when I tell it. It is an old saying that he who tells too much truth is sure to be hanged. I am weary of this argument: we have been over it nine times already. I have sworn as much as I will swear; and I will swear no more.

—COURCELLES. My lord: she should be put to the torture.

—THE INQUISITOR. You hear, Joan? This is what happens to the obdurate. Think before you answer. Has she been shewn the instruments?

—THE EXECUTIONER. They are ready, my lord. She has seen them.

—JOAN. If you tear me limb from limb until you separate my soul from my body you will get nothing out of me beyond what I have told you. What more is there to tell that you could understand? Besides, I cannot bear to be hurt; and if you hurt me I will say anything you like to stop the pain. But I will take it all back afterwards; so what is the use of it?

—LADVENU. There is much in that. We should proceed mercifully.

—COURCELLES. But the torture is customary.

—THE INQUISITOR. It must not be applied wantonly. If the accused will confess voluntarily, then its use cannot be justified.

—COURCELLES. But this is unusual and irregular. She refuses to take the oath.

—LADVENU. [disgusted] Do you want to torture the girl for the mere pleasure of it?

—COURCELLES. [bewildered] But it is not a pleasure. It is the law. It is customary. It is always done.

—THE INQUISITOR. That is not so, Master, except when the inquiries are carried on by people who do not know their legal business.

—COURCELLES.   But the woman is a heretic. I assure you it is always done.

—CAUCHON.   [*decisively*] It will not be done today if it is not necessary. Let there be an end of this. I will not have it said that we proceeded on forced confessions. We have sent our best preachers and doctors to this woman to exhort and implore her to save her soul and body from the fire: we shall not now send the executioner to thrust her into it.

—COURCELLES.   Your lordship is merciful, of course. But it is a great responsibility to depart from the usual practice.

—JOAN.   Thou art a rare noodle, Master. Do what was done last time is thy rule, eh?

—COURCELLES.   [*rising*] Thou wanton; does thou dare call me noodle?

—THE INQUISITOR.   Patience, Master, patience: I fear you will soon be only too terribly avenged.

—COURCELLES.   [*mutters*] Noodle indeed! [*He sits down, much discontented*]

—THE INQUISITOR.   Meanwhile, let us not be moved by the rough side of a shepherd lass's tongue.

—JOAN.   Nay: I am no shepherd lass, though I have helped with the sheep like anyone else. I will do a lady's work in the house—spin or weave—against any woman in Rouen.

—THE INQUISITOR.   This is not a time for vanity, Joan. You stand in great peril.

—JOAN.   I know it: have I not been punished for my vanity? If I had not worn my cloth of gold surcoat in battle like a fool, that Burgundian soldier would never have pulled me backwards off my horse; and I should not have been here.

—THE CHAPLAIN.   If you are so clever at woman's work why do you not stay at home and do it?

—JOAN.   There are plenty of other women to do it; but there is nobody to do my work.

—CAUCHON.   Come! we are wasting time on trifles. Joan: I am going to put a most solemn question to you. Take care how you answer; for your life and salvation are at stake on it. Will

you for all you have said and done, be it good or bad, accept
the judgment of God's Church on earth? More especially as
to the acts and words that are imputed to you in this trial by
the Promoter here, will you submit your case to the inspired
interpretation of the Church Militant?

—JOAN. I am a faithful child of the Church. I will obey
the Church—

—CAUCHON. [*hopefully leaning forward*] You will?

—JOAN. —provided it does not command anything impossible.

*Cauchon sinks back in his chair with a heavy sigh. The
Inquisitor purses his lips and frowns. Ladvenu shakes his
head pitifully.*

—D'ESTIVET. She imputes to the Church the error and folly of
commanding the impossible.

—JOAN. If you command me to declare that all that I have
done and said, and all the visions and revelations I have had,
were not from God, then that is impossible: I will not declare
it for anything in the world. What God made me do I will never
go back on; and what He has commanded or shall command I
will not fail to do in spite of any man alive. That is what I
mean by impossible. And in case the Church should bid me to
do anything contrary to the command I have from God, I will
not consent to it, no matter what it may be.

—THE ASSESSORS. [*shocked and indignant*] Oh! The Church
contrary to God! What do you say now? Flat heresy. This is
beyond everything, etc., etc.

—D'ESTIVET. [*throwing down his brief*] My lord: do you need
anything more than this?

—CAUCHON. Woman: you have said enough to burn ten
heretics. Will you not be warned? Will you not understand?

—THE INQUISITOR. If the Church Militant tells you that your
revelations and visions are sent by the devil to tempt you to
your damnation, will you not believe that the Church is wiser
than you?

—JOAN. I believe that God is wiser than I; and it is His commands that I will do. All the things that you call my crimes have come to me by the command of God. I say that I have done them by the order of God: it is impossible for me to say anything else. If any Churchman says the contrary I shall not mind him: I shall mind God alone, whose command I always follow.

—LADVENU. [*pleading with her urgently*] You do not know what you are saying, child. Do you want to kill yourself? Listen. Do you not believe that you are subject to the Church of God on earth?

—JOAN. Yes. When have I ever denied it?

—LADVENU. Good. That means, does it not, that you are subject to our Lord, the Pope, to the cardinals, the archbishops, and the bishops for whom his lordship stands here today?

—JOAN. God must be served first.

—D'ESTIVET. Then your voices command you not to submit yourself to the Church Militant?

—JOAN. My voices do not tell me to disobey the Church; but God must be served first.

—CAUCHON. And you, and not the Church, are to be the judge?

—JOAN. What other judgment can I judge by but my own?

—THE ASSESSORS. [*scandalized*] Oh! [*They cannot find words*]

—CAUCHON. Out of your own mouth you have condemned yourself. We have striven for your salvation to the verge of sinning ourselves: we have opened the door to you again and again; and you have shut it in our faces and in the face of God. Dare you pretend, after what you have said, that you are in a state of grace?

—JOAN. If I am not, may God bring me to it: if I am, may God keep me in it!

—LADVENU. That is a very good reply, my lord.

—COURCELLES. Were you in a state of grace when you stole the Bishop's horse?

—CAUCHON. [*rising in a fury*] Oh, devil take the Bishop's

horse and you too! We are here to try a case of heresy; and no sooner do we come to the root of the matter than we are thrown back by idiots who understand nothing but horses. [*Trembling with rage, he forces himself to sit down*]

—THE INQUISITOR.   Gentlemen, gentlemen: in clinging to these small issues you are The Maid's best advocates. I am not surprised that his lordship has lost patience with you. What does the Promoter say? Does he press these trumpery matters?

—D'ESTIVET.   I am bound by my office to press everything; but when the woman confesses a heresy that must bring upon her the doom of excommunication, of what consequence is it that she has been guilty also of offences which expose her to minor penances? I share the impatience of his lordship as to these minor charges. Only, with great respect, I must emphasize the gravity of two very horrible and blasphemous crimes which she does not deny. First, she has intercourse with evil spirits, and is therefore a sorceress. Second, she wears men's clothes, which is indecent, unnatural, and abominable; and in spite of our most earnest remonstrances and entreaties, she will not change them even to receive the sacrament.

—JOAN.   Is the blessed St. Catherine an evil spirit? Is St. Margaret? Is Michael the Archangel?

—COURCELLES.   How do you know that the spirit which appears to you is an archangel? Does he not appear to you as a naked man?

—JOAN.   Do you think God cannot afford clothes for him?

The assessors cannot help smiling, especially as the joke is against Courcelles.

—LADVENU.   Well answered, Joan.

—THE INQUISITOR.   It is, in effect, well answered. But no evil spirit would be so simple as to appear to a young girl in a guise that would scandalize her when he meant her to take him for a messenger from the Most High. Joan: the Church instructs you that these apparitions are demons seeking your soul's perdition. Do you accept the instruction of the Church?

—JOAN. I accept the messenger of God. How could any faithful believer in the Church refuse him?

—CAUCHON. Wretched woman: again I ask you, do you know what you are saying?

—THE INQUISITOR. You wrestle in vain with the devil for her soul, my lord: she will not be saved. Now as to this matter of the man's dress. For the last time, will you put off that impudent attire, and dress as becomes your sex?

—JOAN. I will not.

—D'ESTIVET. [*pouncing*] The sin of disobedience, my lord.

—JOAN. [*distressed*] But my voices tell me I must dress as a soldier.

—LADVENU. Joan, Joan: does not that prove to you that the voices are the voices of evil spirits? Can you suggest to us one good reason why an angel of God should give you such shameless advice?

—JOAN. Why, yes: what can be plainer commonsense? I was a soldier living among soldiers. I am a prisoner guarded by soldiers. If I were to dress as a woman they would think of me as a woman; and then what would become of me? If I dress as a soldier they think of me as a soldier, and I can live with them as I do at home with my brothers. That is why St. Catherine tells me I must not dress as a woman until she gives me leave.

—COURCELLES. When will she give you leave?

—JOAN. When you take me out of the hands of the English soldiers. I have told you that I should be in the hands of the Church, and not left night and day with four soldiers of the Earl of Warwick. Do you want me to live with them in petticoats?

—LADVENU. My lord: what she says is, God knows, very wrong and shocking; but there is a grain of worldly sense in it such as might impose on a simple village maiden.

—JOAN. If we were as simple in the village as you are in your courts and palaces, there would soon be no wheat to make bread for you.

—CAUCHON. That is the thanks you get for trying to save her, Brother Martin.

—LADVENU. Joan: we are all trying to save you. His lordship is trying to save you. The Inquisitor could not be more just to you if you were his own daughter. But you are blinded by a terrible pride and self-sufficiency.

—JOAN. Why do you say that? I have said nothing wrong. I cannot understand.

—THE INQUISITOR. The blessed St. Athanasius has laid it down in his creed that those who cannot understand are damned. It is not enough to be simple. It is not enough even to be what simple people call good. The simplicity of a darkened mind is no better than the simplicity of a beast.

—JOAN. There is great wisdom in the simplicity of a beast, let me tell you; and sometimes great foolishness in the wisdom of scholars.

—LADVENU. We know that, Joan: we are not so foolish as you think us. Try to resist the temptation to make pert replies to us. Do you see that man who stands behind you? [he indicates the Executioner]

—JOAN. [turning and looking at the man] Your torturer? But the Bishop said I was not to be tortured.

—LADVENU. You are not to be tortured because you have confessed everything that is necessary to your condemnation. That man is not only the torturer: he is also the Executioner: let The Maid hear your answers to my questions. Are you prepared for the burning of a heretic this day?

—THE EXECUTIONER. Yes, Master.

—LADVENU. Is the stake ready?

—THE EXECUTIONER. It is. In the market-place. The English have built it too high for me to get near her and make the death easier. It will be a cruel death.

—JOAN. [horrified] But you are not going to burn me now?

—THE INQUISITOR. You realize it at last.

—LADVENU. There are eight hundred English soldiers waiting to take you to the market-place the moment the sentence of excommunication has passed the lips of your judges. You are within a few short moments of that doom.

– JOAN. [*looking round desperately for rescue*] Oh God!

– LADVENU. Do not despair, Joan. The Church is merciful. You can save yourself.

– JOAN. [*hopefully*] Yes: my voices promised me I should not be burnt. St. Catherine bade me be bold.

– CAUCHON. Woman: are you quite mad? Do you not yet see that your voices have deceived you?

– JOAN. Oh no: that is impossible.

– CAUCHON. Impossible! They have led you straight to your excommunication, and to the stake which is there waiting for you.

– LADVENU. [*pressing the point hard*] Have they kept a single promise to you since you were taken at Compiègne? The devil has betrayed you. The Church holds out its arms to you.

– JOAN. [*despairing*] Oh, it is true: it is true: my voices have deceived me. I have been mocked by devils: my faith is broken. I have dared and dared; but only a fool will walk into a fire: God, who gave me my commonsense, cannot will me to do that.

– LADVENU. Now God be praised that He has saved you at the eleventh hour! [*He hurries to the vacant seat at the scribes' table, and snatches a sheet of paper, on which he sets to work writing eagerly*]

– CAUCHON. Amen!

– JOAN. What must I do?

– CAUCHON. You must sign a solemn recantation of your heresy.

– JOAN. Sign? That means to write my name. I cannot write.

– CAUCHON. You have signed many letters before.

– JOAN. Yes; but someone held my hand and guided the pen. I can make my mark.

– THE CHAPLAIN. [*who has been listening with growing alarm and indignation*] My lord: do you mean that you are going to allow this woman to escape us?

—THE INQUISITOR. The law must take its course, Master de Stogumber. And you know the law.

—THE CHAPLAIN. [*rising, purple with fury*] I know that there is no faith in a Frenchman. [*tumult, which he shouts down*] I know what my lord the Cardinal of Winchester will say when he hears of this. I know what the Earl of Warwick will do when he learns that you intend to betray him. There are eight hundred men at the gate who will see that this abominable witch is burnt in spite of your teeth.

—THE ASSESSORS. [*meanwhile*] What is this? What did he say? He accuses us of treachery! This is past bearing. No faith in a Frenchman! Did you hear that? That is an intolerable fellow. Who is he? Is this what English Churchmen are like? He must be mad or drunk, etc., etc.

—THE INQUISITOR. [*rising*] Silence, pray! Gentlemen: pray silence! Master Chaplain: bethink you a moment of your holy office: of what you are, and where you are. I direct you to sit down.

—THE CHAPLAIN. [*folding his arms doggedly, his face working convulsively*] I will NOT sit down.

—CAUCHON. Master Inquisitor: this man has called me a traitor to my face before now.

—THE CHAPLAIN. So you are a traitor. You are all traitors. You have been doing nothing but begging this damnable witch on your knees to recant all through this trial.

—THE INQUISITOR. [*placidly resuming his seat*] If you will not sit, you must stand: that is all.

—THE CHAPLAIN. I will NOT stand. [*he flings himself back into his chair*]

—LADVENU. [*rising with the paper in his hand*] My lord: here is the form of recantation for The Maid to sign.

—CAUCHON. Read it to her.

—JOAN. Do not trouble. I will sign it.

—THE INQUISITOR. Woman: you must know what you are putting your hand to. Read it to her, Brother Martin. And let all be silent.

—LADVENU. [*reading quietly*] "I, Joan, commonly called The Maid, a miserable sinner, do confess that I have most grievously sinned in the following articles. I have pretended to have revelations from God and the angels and the blessed saints, and perversely rejected the Church's warnings that these were temptations by demons. I have blasphemed abominably by wearing an immodest dress, contrary to the Holy Scripture and the canons of the Church. Also I have clipped my hair in the style of a man, and, against all the duties which have made my sex specially acceptable in heaven, have taken up the sword, even to the shedding of human blood, inciting men to slay each other, invoking evil spirits to delude them, and stubbornly and most blasphemously imputing these sins to Almighty God. I confess to the sin of sedition, to the sin of idolatry, to the sin of disobedience, to the sin of pride, and to the sin of heresy. All of which sins I now renounce and abjure and depart from, humbly thanking you Doctors and Masters who have brought me back to the truth and into the grace of our Lord. And I will never return to my errors, but will remain in communion with our Holy Church and in obedience to our Holy Father the Pope of Rome. All this I swear by God Almighty and the Holy Gospels, in witness whereto I sign my name to this recantation."

—THE INQUISITOR. You understand this, Joan?

—JOAN. [*listless*] It is plain enough, sir.

—THE INQUISITOR. And it is true?

—JOAN. It may be true. If it were not true, the fire would not be ready for me in the market-place.

—LADVENU. [*taking up his pen and a book, and going to her quickly lest she should compromise herself again*] Come, child: let me guide your hand. Take the pen. [*She does so; and they begin to write, using the book as a desk*] J.E.H.A.N.E. So. Now make your mark by yourself.

—JOAN. [*makes her mark, and gives him back the pen, tormented by the rebellion of her soul against her mind and body*] There!

— LADVENU. [*replacing the pen on the table, and handing the recantation to Cauchon with a reverence*] Praise be to God, my brothers, the lamb has returned to the flock; and the shepherd rejoices in her more than in ninety and nine just persons. [*He returns to his seat*]

— THE INQUISITOR. [*taking the paper from Cauchon*] We declare thee by this act set free from the danger of excommunication in which thou stoodest. [*He throws the paper down to the table*]

— JOAN. I thank you.

— THE INQUISITOR. But because thou hast sinned most presumptuously against God and the Holy Church, and that thou mayst repent thy errors in solitary contemplation, and be shielded from all temptation to return to them, we, for the good of thy soul, and for a penance that may wipe out thy sins and bring thee finally unspotted to the throne of grace, do condemn thee to eat the bread of sorrow and drink the water of affliction to the end of thy earthly days in perpetual imprisonment.

— JOAN. [*rising in consternation and terrible anger*] Perpetual imprisonment! Am I not then to be set free?

— LADVENU. [*mildy shocked*] Set free, child, after such wickedness as yours! What are you dreaming of?

— JOAN. Give me that writing. [*She rushes to the table; snatches up the paper; and tears it into fragments*] Light your fire: do you think I dread it as much as the life of a rat in a hole? My voices were right.

— LADVENU. Joan! Joan!

— JOAN. Yes: they told me you were fools [*the word gives great offence*], and that I was not to listen to your fine words nor trust to your charity. You promised me my life; but you lied. [*indignant exclamations*] You think that life is nothing but not being stone dead. It is not the bread and water I fear: I can live on bread: when have I asked for more? It is no hardship to drink water if the water be clean. Bread has no sorrow for me, and water no affliction. But to shut me from the light of the sky and the sight of the fields and flowers; to chain my feet so that I can never again ride with the soldiers nor climb the hills; to make me breathe foul damp darkness, and keep from me everything that brings me back to the love of God when your wickedness and foolishness tempt me to hate Him: all this is worse than the furnace in the Bible that was heated seven times. I could do without my warhorse; I could drag about in a skirt; I could let the banners and the trumpets and the knights and soldiers pass me and leave me behind as they leave the other women, if only I could still hear the wind in the trees, the larks in the sunshine, the young lambs crying through the healthy frost, and the blessed church bells that send my angel voices floating to me on the wind. But without these things I cannot live; and by your wanting to take them away from me, or from any human creature, I know that your counsel is of the devil, and that mine is of God.

– THE ASSESSORS. [*in great commotion*] Blasphemy! blasphemy! She is possessed. She said our counsel was of the devil. And hers of God. Monstrous. The devil is in our midst, etc., etc.

– D'ESTIVET. [*shouting above the din*] She is a relapsed heretic, obstinate, incorrigible, and altogether unworthy of the mercy we have shewn her. I call for her excommunication.

– THE CHAPLAIN. [*to the Executioner*] Light your fire, man. To the stake with her.

The Executioner and his assistants hurry out through the courtyard.

– LADVENU. You wicked girl: if your counsel were of God would He not deliver you?

– JOAN. His ways are not your ways. He wills that I go through the fire to His bosom; for I am His child, and you are not fit that I should live among you. That is my last word to you.

The soldiers seize her.

– CAUCHON. [*rising*] Not yet.

They wait. There is a dead silence. Cauchon turns to the Inquisitor with an inquiring look. The Inquisitor nods affirmatively. They rise solemnly, and intone the sentence antiphonally.

—CAUCHON. We decree that thou art a relapsed heretic.
—THE INQUISITOR. Cast out from the unity of the Church.
—CAUCHON. Sundered from her body.
—THE INQUISITOR. Infected with the leprosy of heresy.
—CAUCHON. A member of Satan.
—THE INQUISITOR. We declare that thou must be excommunicated.
—CAUCHON. And now we do cast thee out, segregate thee, and abandon thee to the secular power.
—THE INQUISITOR. Admonishing the same secular power that it moderate its judgment of thee in respect of death and division of the limbs. [*He resumes his seat*]
—CAUCHON. And if any true sign of penitence appear in thee, to permit our Brother Martin to administer to thee the sacrament of penance.
—THE CHAPLAIN. Into the fire with the witch. [*He rushes at her, and helps the soldiers to push her out*]

THE JILTING OF GRANNY WEATHERALL

Katherine Anne Porter

She flicked her wrist neatly out of Doctor Harry's pudgy careful fingers and pulled the sheet up to her chin. The brat ought to be in knee breeches. Doctoring around the country with spectacles on his nose! "Get along now, take your schoolbooks and go. There's nothing wrong with me."

Doctor Harry spread a warm paw like a cushion on her forehead where the forked green vein danced and made her eyelids twitch. "Now, now, be a good girl, and we'll have you up in no time."

"That's no way to speak to a woman nearly eighty years old just because she's down. I'd have you respect your elders, young man."

"Well, Missy, excuse me." Doctor Harry patted her cheek. "But I've got to warn you, haven't I? You're a marvel, but you must be careful or you're going to be good and sorry."

"Don't tell me what I'm going to be. I'm on my feet now, morally speaking. It's Cornelia. I had to go to bed to get rid of her."

Her bones felt loose, and floated around in her skin, and Doctor Harry floated like a balloon around the foot of the bed. He floated and pulled down his waistcoat and swung his glasses on a cord. "Well, stay where you are, it certainly can't hurt you."

"Get along and doctor your sick," said Granny Weatherall. "Leave a well woman alone. I'll call for you when I want you. . . . Where were you forty years ago when I pulled through milk leg and double pneumonia? You weren't even born. Don't let Cornelia lead you on," she shouted, because Doctor Harry appeared to float up to the ceiling and out. "I pay my own bills, and I don't throw my money away on nonsense!"

She meant to wave good-by, but it was too much trouble. Her eyes closed of themselves, it was like a dark curtain drawn around the bed. The pillow rose and floated under her, pleasant as a hammock in a light wind. She listened to the leaves rustling outside the window. No, somebody was swishing newspapers: no, Cornelia and Doctor Harry were whispering together. She leaped broad awake, thinking they whispered in her ear.

"She was never like this, *never* like this!" "Well, what can we expect?" "Yes, eighty years old. . . ."

Well, and what if she was? She still had ears. It was like Cornelia to whisper around doors. She always kept things secret in such a public way. She was always being tactful and kind. Cornelia was dutiful; that was the trouble with her. Dutiful and good: "So good and dutiful," said Granny, "that I'd like to spank her." She saw herself spanking Cornelia and making a fine job of it.

"What'd you say, Mother?"

Granny felt her face tying up in hard knots.

"Can't a body think, I'd like to know?"

"I thought you might want something."

"I do. I want a lot of things. First off, go away and don't whisper."

She lay and drowsed, hoping in her sleep that the children would keep out and let her rest a minute. It had been a long day. Not that she was tired. It was always pleasant to snatch a minute now and then. There was always so much to be done, let me see: tomorrow.

Tomorrow was far away and there was nothing to trouble about. Things were finished somehow when the time came; thank God there was always a little margin over for peace: then a person could spread out the plan of life and tuck in the edges orderly. It was good to have everything clean and folded away, with the hairbrushes and tonic bottles sitting straight on the white embroidered linen: the day started without fuss and the pantry shelves laid out with rows of jelly glasses and brown jugs and white stone-china jars with blue whirligigs and words painted on them: coffee, tea, sugar, ginger, cinnamon, allspice: and the bronze clock with the lion on top nicely dusted off. The dust that lion could collect in twenty-four hours! The box in the attic with all those letters tied up, well, she'd have to go through that tomorrow. All those letters—George's letters and John's letters and her letters to them both—lying around for the children to find afterwards made her uneasy. Yes, that would be tomorrow's business. No use to let them know how silly she had been once.

While she was rummaging around she found death in her mind and it felt clammy and unfamiliar. She had spent so much time preparing for death there was no need for bringing it up again. Let it take care of itself now. When she was sixty she had felt very old, finished, and went around making farewell trips to see her children and grandchildren, with a secret in her mind: This is the very last of your mother, children! Then she made her will and came down with a long fever. That was all just a notion like a lot of other things, but it was lucky, too, for she had once and for all got over the idea of dying for a long time. Now she couldn't be worried. She hoped she had better sense now. Her father had lived to see one hundred and two years old and had drunk a noggin of strong hot toddy on his last birthday. He had told the reporters that it was his daily habit, and he owed his long life to that. He had made quite a scandal and was very pleased about it. She believed she'd just plague Cornelia a little.

"Cornelia! Cornelia!" No footsteps, but a sudden hand on her cheek. "Bless you, where have you been?"

"Here, Mother."

"Well, Cornelia, I want a noggin of hot toddy."

"Are you cold, darling?"

"I'm chilly, Cornelia. Lying in bed stops the circulation. I must have told you a thousand times."

Well, she could just hear Cornelia telling her husband that Mother was getting a little childish and they'd have to humor her. The thing that most annoyed her was that Cornelia thought she was deaf, dumb, and blind. Little hasty glances and tiny gestures tossed around her and over her head saying, "Don't cross her, let her have her way, she's eighty years old," and she sitting there as if she lived in a thin glass cage. Sometimes Granny almost made up her mind to pack up and move back to her own house where nobody could remind her every minute that she was old. Wait, wait, Cornelia, till your own children whisper behind your back!

In her day she had kept a better house and had got more work done. She wasn't too old yet for Lydia to be driving eighty miles for advice when one of the children jumped the track, and Jimmy still dropped in and talked things over: "Now, Mammy, you've a good business head, I want to know what you think of this? . . ." Old. Cornelia couldn't change the furniture around without asking. Little things, little things! They had been so sweet when they were little. Granny wished the old days were back again with the children young and everything to be done over. It had been a hard pull, but not too much for her. When she thought of all the food she had cooked, and all the clothes she had cut and sewed, and all the gardens she had made—well, the children showed it. There they were, made out of her, and they couldn't get away from that. Sometimes she wanted to see John again and point to them and say, Well, I didn't do so badly, did I? But that would have to wait. That was for tomorrow. She used to think of him as a man, but now all the children were older than their father, and he would be a child beside her if she saw him now. It seemed strange and there was something wrong in the idea. Why, he couldn't possibly recognize her. She had fenced in a hundred acres once, digging the postholes herself and clamping the wires with just a Negro boy to help. That changed a woman. John would be looking for a young woman with the peaked Spanish comb in her hair and the painted fan.

Digging postholes changed a woman. Riding country roads in the winter when women had their babies was another thing; sitting up nights with sick horses and sick Negroes and sick children and hardly ever losing one. John, I hardly ever lost one of them! John would see that in a minute, that would be something he could understand, she wouldn't have to explain anything!

It made her feel like rolling up her sleeves and putting the whole place to rights again. No matter if Cornelia was determined to be everywhere at once, there were a great many things left undone on this place. She would start tomorrow and do them. It was good to be strong enough for everything, even if all you made melted and changed and slipped under your hands, so that by the time you finished you almost forgot what you were working for. What was it I set out to do? she asked herself intently, but she could not remember. A fog rose over the valley, she saw it marching across the creek swallowing the trees and moving up the hill like an army of ghosts. Soon it would be at the near edge of the orchard, and then it was time to go in and light the lamps. Come in, children, don't stay out in the night air.

Lighting the lamps had been beautiful. The children huddled up to her and breathed like little calves waiting at the bars in the twilight. Their eyes followed the match and watched the flame rise and settle in a blue curve, then they moved away from her. The lamp was lit, they didn't have to be scared and hang on to mother any more. Never, never, never more. God, for all my life I thank Thee. Without Thee, my God, I could never have done it. Hail, Mary, full of grace.

I want you to pick all the fruit this year and see that nothing is wasted. There's always someone who can use it. Don't let good things rot for want of using. You waste life when you waste good food. Don't let things get lost. It's bitter to lose things. Now, don't let me get to thinking, not when I am tired and taking a little nap before supper. . . .

The pillow rose about her shoulders and pressed against her

heart and the memory was being squeezed out of it: oh, push down the pillow, somebody: it would smother her if she tried to hold it. Such a fresh breeze blowing and such a green day with no threats in it. But he had not come, just the same. What does a woman do when she has put on the white veil and set out the white cake for a man and he doesn't come? She tried to remember. No, I swear he never harmed me but in that. He never harmed me but in that . . . and what if he did? There was the day, the day, but a whirl of dark smoke rose and covered it, crept up and over into the bright field where everything was planted so carefully in orderly rows. That was hell, she knew hell when she saw it. For sixty years she had prayed against remembering him and against losing her soul in the deep pit of hell, and now the two things were mingled in one and the thought of him was a smoky cloud from hell that moved and crept in her head when she had just got rid of Doctor Harry and was trying to rest a minute. Wounded vanity, Ellen, said a sharp voice in the top of her mind. Don't let your wounded vanity get the upper hand of you. Plenty of girls get jilted. You were jilted, weren't you? Then stand up to it. Her eyelids wavered and let in streamers of blue-gray light like tissue paper over her eyes. She must get up and pull the shades down or she'd never sleep. She was in bed again and the shades were not down. How could that happen? Better turn over, hide from the light, sleeping in the light gave you nightmares. "Mother, how do you feel now?" and a stinging wetness on her forehead. But I don't like having my face washed in cold water!

Hapsy? George? Lydia? Jimmy? No, Cornelia, and her features were swollen and full of little puddles. "They're coming, darling, they'll all be here soon." Go wash your face, child, you look funny.

Instead of obeying, Cornelia knelt down and put her head on the pillow. She seemed to be talking but there was no sound. "Well, are you tongue-tied? Whose birthday is it? Are you going to give a party?"

Cornelia's mouth moved urgently in strange shapes. "Don't do that, you bother me, daughter."

"Oh, no, Mother. Oh, no. . . ."

Nonsense. It was strange about children. They disputed your every word. "No what, Cornelia?"

"Here's Doctor Harry."

"I won't see that boy again. He just left five minutes ago."

"That was this morning, Mother. It's night now. Here's the nurse."

"This is Doctor Harry, Mrs. Weatherall. I never saw you look so young and happy!"

"Ah, I'll never be young again—but I'd be happy if they'd let me lie in peace and get rested."

She thought she spoke up loudly, but no one answered. A warm weight on her forehead, a warm bracelet on her wrist, and a breeze went on whispering, trying to tell her something. A shuffle of leaves in the everlasting hand of God, He blew on them and they danced and rattled. "Mother, don't mind, we're going to give you a little hypodermic."

"Look here, daughter, how do ants get in this bed? I saw sugar ants yesterday." Did you send for Hapsy too?

It was Hapsy she really wanted. She had to go a long way back through a great many rooms to find Hapsy standing with a baby on her arm. She seemed to herself to be Hapsy also, and the baby on Hapsy's arm was Hapsy and himself and herself, all at once, and there was no surprise in the meeting. Then Hapsy melted from within and turned flimsy as gray gauze and the baby was a gauzy shadow, and Hapsy came up close and said, "I thought you'd never come," and looked at her very searchingly and said, "You haven't changed a bit!" They leaned forward to kiss, when Cornelia began whispering from a long way off, "Oh, is there anything you want to tell me? Is there anything I can do for you?"

Yes, she had changed her mind after sixty years and she would like to see George. I want you to find George. Find him and be sure to tell him I forgot him. I want him to know I had

my husband just the same and my children and my house like
any other woman. A good house too and a good husband that
I loved and fine children out of him. Better than I hoped for
even. Tell him I was given back everything he took away and
more. Oh, no, oh, no, there was something else besides the
house and the man and the children. Oh, surely they were not
all? What was it? Something not given back. . . . Her breath
crowded down under her ribs and grew into a monstrous
frightening shape with cutting edges; it bored up into her
head, and the agony was unbelievable: Yes, John, get the
Doctor now, no more talk, my time has come.

When this one was born it should be the last. The last. It
should have been born first, for it was the one she had truly
wanted. Everything came in good time. Nothing left out, left
over. She was strong, in three days she would be as well as
ever. Better. A woman needed milk in her to have her full
health.

"Mother, do you hear me?"

"I've been telling you—"

"Mother, Father Connolly's here."

"I went to Holy Communion only last week. Tell him I'm
not so sinful as all that."

"Father just wants to speak to you."

He could speak as much as he pleased. It was like him to
drop in and inquire about her soul as if it were a teething
baby, and then stay on for a cup of tea and a round of cards
and gossip. He always had a funny story of some sort, usually
about an Irishman who made his little mistakes and confessed
them, and the point lay in some absurd thing he would blurt
out in the confessional showing his struggles between naive
piety and original sin. Granny felt easy about her soul. Cornelia,
where are your manners? Give Father Connolly a chair. She
had her secret comfortable understanding with a few favorite
saints who cleared a straight road to God for her. All as surely
signed and sealed as the papers for the new Forty Acres.
Forever . . . heirs and assigns forever. Since the day the

wedding cake was not cut, but thrown out and wasted. The whole bottom dropped out of her world, and there she was blind and sweating with nothing under her feet and the walls falling away. His hand had caught her under the breast, and she had not fallen, there was the freshly polished floor with the green rug on it, just as before. He had cursed like a sailor's parrot and said, "I'll kill him for you." Don't lay a hand on him, for my sake leave something to God. "Now, Ellen, you must believe what I tell you. . . ."

So there was nothing, nothing to worry about any more, except sometimes in the night one of the children screamed in a nightmare, and they both hustled out shaking and hunting for the matches and calling, "There, wait a minute, here we are!" John, get the doctor now, Hapsy's time has come. But there was Hapsy standing by the bed in a white cap. "Cornelia, tell Hapsy to take off her cap. I can't see her plain."

Her eyes opened very wide and the room stood out like a picture she had seen somewhere. Dark colors with the shadows rising toward the ceiling in long angles. The tall black dresser gleamed with nothing on it but John's picture, enlarged from a little one, with John's eyes very black when they should have been blue. You never saw him, so how do you know how he looked? But the man insisted the copy was perfect, it was very rich and handsome. For a picture, yes, but it's not my husband. The table by the bed had a linen cover and a candle and a crucifix. The light was blue from Cornelia's silk lamp shades. No sort of light at all, just frippery. You had to live forty years with kerosene lamps to appreciate honest electricity. She felt very strong and she saw Doctor Harry with a rosy nimbus around him.

"You look like a saint, Doctor Harry, and I vow that's as near as you'll ever come to it."

"She's saying something."

"I heard you, Cornelia. What's all this carrying-on."

"Father Connolly's saying—"

Cornelia's voice staggered and bumped like a cart in a bad

road. It rounded corners and turned back again and arrived nowhere. Granny stepped up in the cart very lightly and reached for the reins, but a man sat beside her and she knew him by his hands, driving the cart. She did not look in his face, for she knew without seeing, but looked instead down the road where the trees leaned over and bowed to each other and a thousand birds were singing a Mass. She felt like singing, too, but she put her hand in the bosom of her dress and pulled out a rosary, and Father Connolly murmured Latin in a very solemn voice and tickled her feet. Will you stop that nonsense? I'm a married woman. What if he did run away and leave me to face the priest by myself? I found another a whole world better. I wouldn't have exchanged my husband for anybody except St. Michael himself, and you may tell him that for me with a thank you in the bargain.

Light flashed on her closed eyelids, and a deep roaring shook her. Cornelia, is that lightning? I hear thunder. There's going to be a storm. Close all the windows. Call the children in. . . . "Mother, here we are, all of us." "Is that you, Hapsy?" "Oh, no, I'm Lydia. We drove as fast as we could." Their faces drifted above her, drifted away. The rosary fell out of her hands and Lydia put it back. Jimmy tried to help, their hands fumbled together, and Granny closed two fingers around Jimmy's thumb. Beads wouldn't do, it must be something alive. She was so amazed her thoughts ran round and round. So, my dear Lord, this is my death and I wasn't even thinking about it. My children have come to see me die. But I can't, it's not time. Oh, I always hated surprises. I wanted to give Cornelia the amethyst set—but Hapsy's to wear it when she wants, and, Doctor Harry, do shut up. Nobody sent for you. Oh, my dear Lord, do wait a minute. I meant to do something about the Forty Acres, Jimmy doesn't need it and Lydia will later on, with that worthless husband of hers. I meant to finish the altar cloth and send six bottles of wine to Sister Borgia for her dyspepsia. I want to send six bottles of wine to Sister Borgia, Father Connolly, now don't let me forget.

Cornelia's voice made short turns and lilted over and crashed. "Oh, Mother, oh, Mother, oh, Mother. . . ."

"I'm not going, Cornelia. I'm taken by surprise. I can't go."

You'll see Hapsy again. What about her? "I thought you'd never come." Granny made a long journey outward, looking for Hapsy. What if I don't find her. What then? Her heart sank down and down, there was no bottom to death, she couldn't come to the end of it. The blue light from Cornelia's lamp shade drew into a tiny point in the center of her brain, it flickered and winked like an eye, quietly it fluttered and dwindled. Granny lay curled down within herself, amazed and watchful, staring at the point of light that was herself; her body was now only a deeper mass of shadow in an endless darkness and this darkness would curl around the light and swallow it up. God, give a sign!

For the second time there was no sign. Again no bridegroom and the priest in the house. She could not remember any other sorrow because this grief wiped them all away. Oh, no, there's nothing more cruel than this—I'll never forgive it. She stretched herself with a deep breath and blew out the light.

THE DEVIL IN THE DESERT

Paul Horgan

One summer morning almost a hundred years ago in the town
of Brownsville near the mouth of the Rio Grande on the Gulf
of Mexico, Father Pierre Arnoud awoke before dawn in great
distress.

"Yesterday," he said to himself bitterly, "I should have told
him yesterday."

He listened in the dark of his room whose little window was
just showing the first pearly ghost of day over the Gulf. Yes, he
would hear what he dreaded to hear. Deep in the house were
sounds of footsteps moving about. Father Pierre could tell
where those steps went, and what their maker was doing. Now
he was in the study taking up certain printed materials—a
breviary, a missal, a handful of ornately printed blanks for
baptisms, marriages, and first communions, which could be
filled in as occasion required. The footsteps receded toward the
refectory, and there a battered leather knapsack soon was
being filled with a cheese, two loaves of bread, a little sack of
dried meal, a flask of red wine, and a jug of water. Presently,
a distant door opened and closed and the footsteps went
across the paved garden to the side door of the sacristy in the
church, where another leather case would be stocked with
sacred vessels, holy oils, communion wafers, and a set of
vestments made in France of thin silk from Lyons. The sacristy
door sounded again, and Father Pierre knew that the next
stage of all these preparations for a journey would move out
beyond the rectory and the church to the ragged field where in
a corral the two priests of the parish kept their horses. There,
he knew, Pancho, the eight-year-old gelding who was the

colour of rusty weeds along the river, was going to be captured after an absurd moment of delicacy and apprehension, saddled, and brought back to the courtyard where the saddlebags and knapsacks were waiting. By then it would be light enough outdoors to see where you were going. It would be time to go.

From the sounds he could hear and the activities he could imagine, Father Pierre knew all over again something of the formidable man who was getting ready to depart. If those footsteps sounded like those of an old man, trotting and tentative, yet there was in them a stubborn force. There was plain contempt for human comfort in the noise he made before dawn when others might be sleeping; but he seemed to say that if one man could get up to make all that noise in the name of God then any other should be glad to awaken to it.

Father Pierre knew there was grim joy in the world that morning for his friend and colleague Father Louis Belle-fontaine. He knew also that Father Louis tried to control a capacity for anger that could flare as quickly and as madly as a cat's. In the new stone rectory the two men lived harmoniously for the most part. It took much government of their natural temperaments to make this possible, for over everything lay the difficulty that Father Pierre, who was many years the younger, was the pastor; while Father Louis, who had come from France a generation before Father Pierre, was the assistant, and so subject to the orders of his junior. But they made jokes about this, as they did about Father Pierre's education. Father Louis knew only his God, his duties, and what he had learned from hard contests with nature. He knew it was proper for a fine gentleman like Father Pierre to be his superior; and he would wrinkle his old face with shrewd estimate and relish of silken details when Father Pierre was busy with narratives about life at home—which meant France, where one day without doubt the younger priest would be consecrated a bishop. But Father Louis never envied his superior anything, for he knew that in his own work he was a great master—a master of the distance, the heat, the fatigue, the menace of time in slow travel, the harsh vegetation of the brush desert, the murderous Indian whose soul was within him but not yet formed, the fears, hopes, and needs of the Christian families who lived so widely separated, along the inland course of the Rio Grande. For thirty years Father Louis had ridden, mostly alone, and twice a year, on his journeys up the river.

He always undertook them with a sense not only of duty but of escape. Nowhere else did he feel so close to God as alone in the hard brush country riding to bring comfort, news, and the sacraments to some family in a *jacal* hidden by solitude open to the hot sky. The older he grew, the more Father Louis longed for his escapes from town and parish. The more infirm he became with the years, the stronger was his sense of mission. Father Pierre would see a glow of youth come back over that sun-stung, seamed old face as time drew near for Father Louis to make his plans to go on his ride into the upriver country, which would take him from two to three months. If his eyes were dim with age, not so the vision in his mind, which showed him so much of what people wanted of him, and of what he could bring to them. If his hand now trembled so that he could hardly write down the names and dates on one of his sacramental certificates, he could always joke about it, and assure his families that the deed was recorded in Heaven, anyway. If sometimes his heart fluttered like a dusty bird in the cage of his ribs, and made him wonder what was ready to take flight, he could lie down for a few minutes and feel the thing calm itself; and however unworldly he may have been, he always clamped his jaws together with sardonic satisfaction that his time had not yet quite come. He had things to do, and would do them.

Much of this was known to Father Pierre by intuition, and he recalled it as he arose this morning. He hastened, for if he was going to catch Father Louis and say to him what should have been said yesterday, and even long before that, he would have to hurry. Do you suppose it could be, thought Father Pierre, that I am afraid of him? Or am I afraid for my dignity?

What if he simply will not listen to me? He has pretended before this to be deaf like an old man when he has preferred not to hear me. Or do I not want to see a look of pain in his small, old, blue eyes? Actually, is there not a possibility that what I must tell him will shock him so that it might make him ill?

Father Pierre shrugged angrily at his doubts and tried to answer them reasonably.

Nonsense. After all, a letter from the bishop has approved my decision and given me authority to do what is wise. Why must I heed for a second the individual feelings of anyone, myself included, when a duty is to be done? If I have been a coward for days, in spite of all my prayers for strength and enlightenment on how best to do what needs doing, must I not be doubly strong today?

And yet, as he went downstairs and out to the courtyard where a rosy daylight seemed to emerge from the ochre limestone of the church wall and glow in the very air, Father Pierre was as never before conscious of the difference in years between him and the old man who was at this moment hauling at straps and buckles, with one knee raised against Pancho's belly to brace himself.

It was a picture, as Father Pierre could not help pausing to notice.

The horse was laden, ready and patient. His summer coat was nicely brushed. His bridle was of woven horsehair. His saddle was bulky and tall, with some of the leather worn away so that the wooden forms of horn and cantle showed through. That saddle was chair and pillow, living-room and crutch to Father Louis. To it he had attached many ingenious and cranky accessories, among which there was nowhere any provision for carrying a weapon. Father Louis went unarmed.

The old priest was dressed in a long homespun coat and heavy trousers. On his head was a woven cane hat with a wide brim under which his face, peering around at Father Pierre, looked like a crab apple underneath a shelf. His boots were

high, the colour of dried clay. Now, in the presence of the
younger man, he redoubled his efforts at finishing his preparations. He made extra movements to show how difficult the
job was, and he completed them with a little flourish to show
how easily he overcame all. His breath went fast, making his
voice dry and thin when he spoke.

"Well, Pierre, I am just about off. I hoped I'd see you before I went."

Father Pierre laughed. His heart beat. He said to himself,
Now, now, I must tell him now. But he heard himself reply
only,

"How did you think anybody could sleep with all your
racket?"

"Ha."

It was a dry, indifferent comment. And then Father Louis
looked sharply into his superior's eyes. What he saw there
made him hurry.

"Well, I have everything. I'll send word back to you, if I
meet anybody coming this way."

Father Louis began to slap at his breast-pockets with sudden
dismay.

"Oh, Pierre, think of it. I nearly forgot my sun-glasses, the
new ones, you know the pair, which my niece sent to me from
Vitry-le-François?"

"I have seen them, yes. They have green glass and metal
rims, I believe?"

"The ones! Would you be a good angel and just get them
for me? They must be in my room."

"You'll wait for me?"

"But of course."

"I'll be right back."

How could it be; and yet it was. Father Pierre, at the very
point of discharging his sorry duty, was sent off on an errand
by his victim. He shook his head. What did he fear so? The
mere rage of Father Louis? The years of unspoken submission
of the older man to the younger? The human aches that can

invade the hearts even of those promised to God? He didn't know. All he could believe was that the unshaven knobbled old man waiting down there by his packed horse, with his hands that trembled on a regular slow beat, and his old blue eyes, was stronger than he. Father Pierre was tall and slender and chiselled in man's noble likeness. His soutane was always clean. His white face and dark eyes could blaze with the Holy Ghost. He had proper respect for authority, but could not now use his own.

Lifting piles of papers, and putting aside apples that had dried up, and mineral specimens blanched by dust, he searched Father Louis' room for the green sun-glasses with their oval lenses and tin rims. He smiled at the condition of the room. He did not find the glasses. He returned to the courtyard.

Father Louis was already in the saddle. In his hand he held the sun-glasses.

"I found them," he said. "I am sorry you had to go for them. Good-bye, Pierre. Give me your blessing. I must be getting along now."

Through his thin old voice, and his clouded eyes, there spoke a boy who was off to a picnic. Father Pierre's heart sank as he looked at him. He knew now that he was not going to tell what it was his duty to tell. Chagrined at his own weakness, and touched by the joy in the face of the impatient old man, he lifted his hand and blessed him with the sign of the Cross, to which Father Louis bent his body, leaning forward with the elegance which, no matter what they may be on the ground, men used to the saddle assume the minute they are mounted. Then with a tart smile on his face under the woven cane hat, Father Louis waved grandly to his superior, turned his reins, and at a rapid hilarious walk was taken by his willing horse out of the courtyard and down the road toward the river, where the first light of the sun lapped at the brown ruffled water which came from so far beyond even the country where he was going.

II

After all these years he had a map in his head. The river came
on a long diagonal, so. An old Indian trail went off north-
westward at another angle, so. The farther inland, the farther
apart they were from one another. There was one kind of
country here by the sea-coast. Presently it changed to another
kind. Finally, in the distance of weeks, where the map would
have only faltering scratches of the pen, based on rumour and
legend, lay the farthest wilderness of Father Louis' journeys.
The natural limits of his endurance were determined by water.
His private map had an X for the end of each stage of travel—a
settlement, a farm, a creek, a spring, a water-hole (and pray it
was not dry).

For the first several days, on these journeys, he hardly
seemed to have left home. The earth was still low and sandy,
and he could read in it how epochs ago the sea itself was here,
hauling and grinding the stuff of ocean bottoms where now he
rode. The air was moist and little clouds came to be and to
vanish almost before his gaze. He could not closely follow the
river for it wandered and turned, in some places doubling back
upon itself in its last exhausted efforts to reach the sea. And so
he followed the Indian trail, leaving it only to go to the
isolated river farms in turn.

At such a one he might spend the night, or longer, depend-
ing upon what he found. Sometimes death approached in the
family, and he gave the last sacraments. Sometimes there were
infants to baptize. In the mornings under a tree at rough-hewn
planks set across a pair of hogsheads he would say Mass and
give communion. He listened to the local news from Mexico
across the Rio Grande—there was talk of another war between
the ranchers of Coahuila and the Mexican troops; it had not
rained for a hundred and seventy days; robbers came over the
river a while back and killed four men here in Texas and stole

some cattle and horses and went back across the river; a child was born in the Bolson de Mapimi who spoke, quite clearly, at three days old, of a flood that would come but who, when further questioned, seemed to have lost the power of speech; and so on. Father Louis in his turn told how things were at Brownsville, and farther up the coast at Corpus Christi and Galveston, and across the sea in France, where under the new emperor business was booming, and trade with Mexico was growing, as you could tell by the many ships that came from Marseilles and Le Havre into the Gulf of Mexico. And then after receiving gifts of food from such a family, the rider left the river and returned to the trail, going north-westward once more.

Days later, though the sky did not cool during the day-time, the quality of the heat changed, and was dry, as the old sea-coast plain gave way to a wilderness of rolling country thickly covered with thorny brush. When he encountered it as it wandered, the river bed was rocky, and rock showed through the hard, prickly ground. Everywhere he looked he saw only that endless roll of empty land. Here, near to him, it was speckled with the colours of the olive, both green and ripe, but not with any of the grace he remembered from long ago in southern France, where the olive trees gave a silver sweetness to the landscape. Farther away in the distance, the land rolls swam in glassy heat. Way off at the horizon there was a stripe of hazy blue where the hot white sky met the earth. Nowhere could he see a mountain, either in Mexico or in Texas.

As he rode, the country tried to hold him back. The thorns of the mesquite dragged at his boots and tore his clothes. Pancho was clever at avoiding most of the hazards, but in places these were so thick that all they could do, man and horse, was to go slowly and stoutly through them. But this was nothing new. Father Louis had persisted before against the thorns and had prevailed.

As for water, there was always too much or too little. Too little when, after years of drought, certain springs he looked forward to would, as he came upon them, reveal only dried white stones. Too much when, in hot spells so violent that they could only be ended with violence, there would be a cloudburst and the heavens would fall almost solid and bring the first water which as it struck the baked earth actually hissed and made crackling sounds until the varnished desert was slaked enough to receive the water in its fissures and let it run. When it ran in such quantity, every finger-like draw became a torrent in which a man and a horse could easily be drowned. If he crossed one in safety, another was waiting to engulf him beyond the next roll. There was no place for shelter. When the rain stopped, the sun came back and dried everything the same day except the running arroyos, which went dry the next day. All too soon there was bitter dust that sparkled in the light and rose with the hot wind. Against it Father Louis tied across his face his great bandanna that came from New Orleans.

And they went on, making a small shadow of horse and man moving slowly yet certainly across that huge empty map where days apart, each from the other, little clusters of human life and need clung to being and shone in Father Louis' mind and purpose like lanterns in the darkness—which usually was the first image he saw of his destination when by his reckoning it was time to reach another of his families.

Was this a hard journey?

Very well, then, it was a hard journey.

But so was the life hard that he found at the end of each stage of his travels. He had seen men grow old and die in his visits here, and their sons with their wives bring new souls to this wilderness in turn. They learned severe lessons in isolation, heat, and the hostility of the animal and vegetable world. Everyone, the child, the grandfather, the husband, the wife, the youth, the horse, the maiden, worked unceasingly against dust, thorn, ignorance, and scarcity from dawn to dark. The great world was but a rumour here, and, by the time it came to the brush deserts, mostly wrong. But a world without limits of dimension dwelt behind the eyes of all those parched, brown people obedient to the natural terms of their lives. It was the world of the human soul, in which could live promises so beautiful and satisfactions so full of ease that the hardships and the betrayals of impersonal nature could be survived, if only someone came from time to time with the greatest news in all life.

For Father Louis knew in a simple flatness of fact—fact as hard as rock, as mysterious as water, as dazzling as light—that without God the richest life in the world was more arid than the desert; and with Him the poorest life was after all complete in a harmony that composed all things. To be the agent of such a composition put upon him a duty in the light of which all peril on his journeys became at worst mere inconvenience. Everyone he toiled overland to see needed and deserved that which he, at the moment, under existing circumstances, alone could bring. In a very practical way he was still awed by the mystery of his office. And as a human being he could never deny himself the joy it gave him to see in their faces what his coming meant to his people in the harsh wilderness. They knew what he had come through. They were proud to be thought worth such labour and danger. They loved him.

His mind was active in the solitude through which he crawled day after day mounted on Pancho. One of his favourite fancies was this, that a great triangle existed between God in Heaven and any little ranch toward which he rode through the days and himself. It was an always changing triangle, for one of its points was not fixed: his own. As he came nearer and nearer to his goal of the moment, the great hypotenuse between himself and God grew shorter and shorter, until at the last, when he arrived, there was a straight line with all in achieved communion. He smiled over this idea, but he respected it, too; and sometimes he would take a piece of charcoal from a fire and draw a series of pictures of what he meant, explaining it to the people he was visiting, and they would murmur, and nod, and consult each other, and enjoy the notion with him, marvelling.

One day at noon on the present journey he knew he should soon see what would look like a long thin blade of cloud shadow far ahead on the earth that slowly quivered with wafts of light like those in wavering mirrors. But it was not a cloud shadow, as he had found out nearly thirty years ago. It was the distant gash of a long canyon whose yellow rock walls were stained with great stripes of slate blue. It came from the north and far away to the south opened into the rocky trough of the Rio Grande. In its bottom were all the signs of a river but running water. Here and there were shallow pools fed by the underground flow which needed storm water to call it continuously to the surface. Father Louis always paused at such a pool for a bath. There were sores on his body from the catch of thorns through which he rode. Sometimes a needle of the brush would break in his flesh and burrow its way under his skin. For the most part he was unaware of such an affliction, but by its comfort the warm alkaline water of the pool reminded him of the misery he had forgotten to notice. It was usually mid-afternoon by the time he reached the canyon wall as the sun went lower. The place was like a palace to him, open to the brassy sky. Wrens and hawks came to look at him in their wary turns. To be below the surface of the rolling plain in the canyon was to have for a little while the luxury of privacy, somehow. He bathed, and dozed as he dried, and sat in the shade reading his breviary. He knew when it was just time to gather himself together and resume his ride in order to come by nightfall to the house and the spring of Encarnadino Guerra, where he would spend the night.

This friend was a boy of ten when Father Louis first met him. He was now the father of six children, the husband of a silent, smiling woman named Cipriana, the son of a widowed mother called Dona Luz who on his last visit told Father Louis she would not live to enjoy his next one. He remembered how she sat blinking in the brilliant shade of the desert bowing to him over and over, while a triumph of patience went over her face eroded by time and trouble and work and pain, as she said,

"At night, when everything is quiet, and I am awake and alone, for I cannot sleep much any more, something speaks to me, and tells me to be ready, and not to make any other plans."

She looked at him with hardly any light in her small eyes, and he knew she was right. When he said Mass for them that time, he thought he saw in her face some powerful, direct understanding of the holy sacrifice which during all her pious life had slumbered within her but which at last came clear in her whole, small, withered being.

He wondered whether through any dry, desert-like tenacity she might still be living.

But when he rode up in the arching twilight to the dwelling of the Guerras, almost the first thing they told him after their excited greeting was that Dona Luz had died early in the summer while sitting in the shade on her bench holding her stick of ocotillo wood which her hands had shined so smooth.

In the light of the candle lantern the family looked at him and then at each other. They were shocked by how he had changed since last year. He was stooped and he slowly trembled all the time. He had to peer at them to see them, even though he preserved a smile to make nothing of this. Burned by the wind and sun, his face looked smaller. He breathed shallowly, with his mouth a little open. He seemed to them a very old man, all of a sudden.

It was like a secret they must keep from him.

After their first start, they got busy making his supper. The younger children lost their shyness and came from behind chairs and the edges of the table to see him, and at last to climb upon him. He smelled dry and dusty to them, like the earth.

After supper he held lessons in catechism for the younger

children, who tomorrow would receive their first communions. The parents and the two older sons listened also.

After that, there was a little time left for gossip. The family's news was all of the seasons. The priest's was boiled down out of letters and newspapers from France. The Guerras already knew that the earthly love of his life was his native country, which he had not seen for over thirty years, but which still spoke in his darting eyes, his cleverness at description, and in the accent with which he spoke Spanish. They listened respectfully while he made picture after picture in his talk of what he loved and missed; but they could not really see with him either the cool green fields, the ancient stone farmhouses, the lanes of poplar trees, the clear rivers, or the proud old towns, or the glorious towering cathedrals, or the silvery web of his dear city of Paris sparkling delicately in day-time, glowing in the long dusk with golden lamps and violet distance.

But they were honoured simply to have him here, and stared before his marvels, and held their breath for tomorrow, when he would give them sacraments.

In the morning he visited the grave of Dona Luz. Everybody went with him. She was buried a little way off from the adobe house. When he saw how little earth she displaced, he nodded and smiled, as though meeting all over again her modest character which he knew so well. Guerra brought some water in an earthen vessel, not much, but enough. Father Louis took the jug and held it in both hands a moment, and gazed into it. They were all reminded of how precious water was on the earth, how it determined by its presence the very presence of life. Then he blessed it, and they all knew what this meant in terms of their daily struggle. Then, reciting prayers for the dead, he walked around the small mound of the grandmother and sprinkled the holy water upon it, and they knew he was keeping once again a promise made between heaven and earth a long time ago.

After that they returned to the house and he took them one by one and heard them confess their sins, of which as they were contrite he relieved them. Then, at an altar improvised against the wall where the old woman used to sit for so many hours, he said Mass, wearing his embroidered French silks, and using the pewter chalice that came out of his saddlebag. The family knelt on the ground in a straight line facing the altar. The famous triangle of Father Louis was brought into a straight line also. God and mankind were made one. As he recited the words during the offertory, "Oh, God, Who has established the nature of man in wondrous dignity, and even more wondrously has renewed it . . . ," Father Louis felt behind him the bodily presences of that isolated family, and an almost bitter sense of the dearness of each of their souls humbled him at his altar.

When Mass was over, they returned within the house, where, at the raw table polished by countless unnoticed contacts of all the family, Father Louis sat down to fill in certificates of first communion for the younger children. He had a flask of guizache ink and a German steel pen. Sitting as far back from the documents as he could the better to read, he began to write. A look of disgust came over his face as his trembling hand gave him trouble. Exclaiming impatiently, he put his left hand on his right wrist to add strength and steadiness where they were needed; but this did not help much, and when he was done, he pushed the papers toward the head of the family saying,

"Nobody ever can read my writing except God."

They all took him seriously, prouder than before of their papers.

"But that is enough, isn't it?" he demanded in comic ferocity.

They had a merry breakfast when all talked as though they would not soon again have a chance to talk, which was true; all except Guerra, who was going to speak of something as soon as he had built up enough of his own silence. Finally he was ready.

"Father," he said, leaning back a trifle in his chair, and half closing his eyes to disguise deep feelings, "you won't be going on anywhere else, after us, will you?"

"Oh, yes."

"Where will you go, Father?"

"Why, I plan to ride from here over toward the river—I have a couple of families over there—and I may go as far as the town of San Ygnacio, to see if the priests from Mier are making visits there, as they ought to. Why?"

Guerra put his head on one side and shrugged.

He did not want to say that the old man was exhausted and ought not to go so far in the pitiless country under the searing sun. It would not be polite to say the old man was older than his years, and he must be seventy anyway. He might be misunderstood if he said that everybody reached a time after a life of hard work when he must pause and rest and let stronger people do what needed doing. It would hardly do to show outright that he thought Father Louis should give up, and stay here, and rest a few weeks, and then perhaps Encarnadino Guerra might leave everything here in the hands of his two strong, quiet boys, and just ride with Father Louis until he saw him safely back in Brownsville.

Father Louis peered close to his younger friend and saw enough of these thoughts to stir him up.

"Eh?" he cried, rapping hard with his knuckles on Guerra's skull, "what goes on in there?" He was sharp and angry. What were they all thinking? That he was a feeble old man? He knew all there was to know about that; but if anything was to be said about it, he, not they, or anybody else, was the one to say it. "Mind your manners, you, boy," he said to Guerra, screwing up his small eyes until all that showed of them were two sharp blue points of light. "Eh? You have opinions, have you? Who told you to think anything! Eh? When I want you to think anything about anybody, I'll tell you. Eh? I got here, didn't I? How many times have I managed to come? And what for! Does anybody tell me to come? Or where to go? Or when? Or why? Then you keep your place, and thank God for your blessings, and for your friends, and understand that it is just as bad to hold an impolite thought as it is to say an impolite thing. Eh?" His whole body shook with the passion he failed to control. "Bad. You'd just better be careful, that's all I have to say, do you hear?"

The family were appalled at this burst of feeling. They sat with downcast eyes, fearing that it would be disrespectful to look upon Father Louis in his rage. But they had little glimpses of his unshaven face whitened with anger, and they could hear how pulse-shaken his voice was. Guerra was more Indian than anything else, and his countenance became fixed. He leaned back, let his eyelids cut his gaze in half, and took his dressing-down without response. He was not even hurt by it. He knew why it came to him. He knew how much it proved him right in his concern. He admired the flare of spirit in the old man. He was at peace with himself for trying what he had tried.

The youngest child, not understanding what had taken place, now, belatedly, felt the emotion among all the older ones, and turning up her little clay-doll face she burst into wails of misery and fear, bringing her tiny creature-paws to her howling mouth until she resembled the small sculptured masks of earth buried with the dead centuries ago deep in Mexico.

Father Louis roughly took her upon his lap. He bent his bristly face close to hers, cactus and blossom together, and in barely audible murmurs quieted the child, and himself, which took about five minutes.

This act reclaimed them all for each other. Once again the visitor was kind and smiling, and the family without fear.

"And so, good-bye for this time," said Father Louis, putting the child down and standing up. "If you will get my horse for me?"

Guerra spoke to one of the boys, who went to fetch Pancho. They all met him outside. Cipriana brought some tortillas for the saddlebag. Everyone knelt down to be blessed. The hot sunlight smote them. They had lingered over their breakfast.

It was late. Father Louis, mounted and ready, blessed them three times, and then turned and rode off to the south. After a while he looked back. They were still kneeling. The next time he looked back it was hard to see them, for at even a little distance they made the same shadows as the scrubby bushes that grew on the caked earth, and seemed just as eternally rooted there.

He had a bad morning.

The sun seemed hotter to him than before. The savage brush seemed animated with spite as it clawed at his legs going by. Pancho, after a lifetime in the brush country, took it into his head to be terrified of familiar things, and from time to time, without warning, executed a rapid dance step to one side while throwing his head back and rolling his eyes at his rider.

"Hush, you fool!" Father Louis exclaimed at such times. "You fool!"

But he addressed himself as much as he did the horse. For the first few hours of that day's ride, he reviewed many times the loss of temper at Guerra, and developed a masterly case, closely reasoned, lucid as only a French argument could be, compassionate with a largeness of heart, yet as logical as music in its progression, about why it had been not only natural, but actually necessary to reprove Guerra for having presumed to hold views about him. Reprove? Perhaps actually more of a scolding. Scolding? Thinking it over, possibly even a tongue-lashing. And the knuckles? The furious raps on the head? Still, how else could he be made to understand? But understand what?

It was no good.

As he always did, in the end, he lost the argument with himself. He knew that after hours of exhausting search for conclusions that would excuse him for what he had done, he would at last come to the truth, which was that he had offended God and man through his lifelong besetting sins of pride, self-esteem, and attempted condonement of his own shortcomings; and that there would be nothing left to do but go down upon his knees and admit how wrong he had been and pray to be forgiven and to be granted strength once more to conquer himself.

He began his penance with a resolve not to eat or drink until nightfall.

By mid-afternoon, the brush grew thicker. Only occasionally did he come to a little clearing between the mesquite bushes, which rose higher than himself mounted on Pancho. In spite of his green sun-glasses, the ground sparkled and glared enough to hurt his eyes. He watched for but he could not see the long pale blur which would tell him that another canyon lay ahead which he would follow until it took him finally to the Rio Grande. He kept the sun on his right, for it was declining in the west in the white sky and he was going south. The day was still.

But how was this?

He thought he heard a singing wind, but when he tried to notice whether he could feel the air stirring, or see dust rising ahead of him, there was no sign of wind. He halted Pancho. What did he hear, then? He turned his head. Yes, he could hear something, now far ahead, now here in his very ear. He searched the undulating horizon but he saw nothing except the wavering image of heat where the white sky met the dusty earth.

As he rode on, the singing in the air became louder. It sounded like the voice of the desert heat. He shook his head, resentful of natural conditions that hid behind mystery. And then suddenly he knew, and scornfully he rebuked himself for taking so long about it.

He was riding into a swarm of cicadas, and now he could see the first ones, clinging to the mesquite as they raised their shrieking song of the heat. The farther he rode the louder they became. He bent his head under their stinging assault upon his hearing. There were thousands and millions of them.

Blindly they fulfilled their natures in their collective scream of response to the sun and the desert. The very atmosphere seemed to be in flames, and the sound of the stridulating insects added to the illusion.

Father Louis had touched the desert often enough. He had smelled it. He had tasted it when its dust rose on the wind. He had seen it in every state. But never before in so real sense had he heard it.

He was suddenly exhausted.

In a clearing, a little lake of baked dust a few yards in diameter, he halted and dismounted, tying Pancho to a stout mesquite branch. Disturbed, a cloud of cicadas rose in crackling threads of flight and found another bush. The ringing sound rose all about him. He could not even hear the sound of Pancho stamping his foot to shake off flies. He clapped his hands, but made barely a sound against the strident song in the air. He felt removed from himself. All desert natures combined to render him impersonal. Here, humbled not only from within but from without, he could find real contrition. He knelt down to pray.

Sunlight was brilliant in the centre of the clearing, a little open room hidden by time, distance, and mesquite clumps. At the west side of it there was lacy shade, cast by tall bushes. But Father Louis rejected it and knelt in the plain sunlight. He bent his head under the beat of his spirit and of the insect scream which seemed to invoke the zenith. He prayed to be forgiven for his miserable anger.

His thoughts came alive in French, the language through which he had first met God.

He was not long now at his contritions, for he knew that prayer was not so often a matter of length as of depth. Much sobered, even saddened, by his intense self-discovery, he arose wearily from his knees and went over to the shade to lie down. He went as deeply as he could into the underboughs of the thorny mesquite. He closed his eyes. At once he felt cooler, just to have the hot light shaded from his sight. Ah, this was delicious, just to lie for a few moments and gather strength to go on for the remaining hours of daylight. He felt how his limbs all went heavy on the earth as he let himself drift off to sleep.

Little coins of light fell over him through the intricate branches. Where he lay, he made solid shadow himself under the mesquite tree. He was as quiet and substantial as a rock. And if he used nature, it in turn used him, without his knowing, for he was asleep.

He did not see, or smell, or feel what came in slow inquiry along the trackless ground, striving forward in orderly, powerful progress, flowing in a dry glitter and advancing through always new and always repeated thrust of form from side to side and yet ahead. It was a diamond-back rattlesnake in search of shade and cool. It came from deep in the scattered brush, and it found the heavy sleeping man under the bushy tree. With what seemed almost conscious caution against awakening the sleeper, the snake drew closer and closer in infinite delicacy, until in the shade of Father Louis' right shoulder it lay heavily at rest, its length doubled back and forth in inert splendour.

The sleepers did not stir for a while; and then Father Louis grew tense in dream, his mouth fell open, and awakening with a jerk he sat up, lost in forgetfulness of where he was or how he came there. He stared at the white sky.

The thick snake at the first quiver of motion beside itself drew instantly into its coil and shook its dozen rattles.

Their dry buzz could not be heard over the general din of the cicadas.

"Ah, yes," sighed Father Louis, as he discovered where he was, and why, and whither he was going. He put his hand to his brow and sank roughly back to the earth to take a few more minutes of rest. The snake struck him in the shoulder and struck him again. Its coils turned dust into liquid light as they lashed. The strikes came like blows made by the thick, powerful arm of a young man.

"What then?" said Father Louis at the sudden stabbing pain and the blows that shook him. He first thought of mesquite thorns on a springy branch; they were long and, as he had often said, sharp as fangs, and their prick could fester if not treated. It occurred to him that this would be troublesome now, as he could hardly reach his own shoulder to wash, cut open the skin, and dig out the thorns if they had broken to stay in the flesh.

But he turned to see the branch that had attacked him, and saw the snake instead.

The snake was retreating. He could see its eye with its glaring drop of light. His heart began to beat hard. He had a surge of rage. He wanted to kill the snake, and actually rose to one knee and scraped the ground with his hands for something to attack with—a rock, a club of dead wood, anything—but he could find nothing. He sank down again and out of habit in any crisis brought his hands together with crossed thumbs in the attitude of prayer.

"No, no, no anger," he besought of himself with his eyes shut. He had just endured and come through a storm of his own pride, and he must not now create another. He opened his eyes and looked after the snake, and saw where it paused half in, half out of the dappled shade of the next bush.

"Go," he said to it.

What he meant by this came to be more and more clear through calm and struggle in the next hour or so. The snake, as though it heard him, resumed in infinite slowness the gliding flow of its retreat until it was lost to sight among the hot thickets where the insects still sang and sang.

"Yes, go," he repeated bitterly, and was ashamed to discover that he was weeping. It was the humanity in him that wept because death was coming. He fell over upon his face and put his cracked and dusty hands over his eyes. His mouth was open and he took into it the loose acid earth with his breath. His tears ran down his fingers. His heart was pounding rapidly upon the ground. It seemed to shake the earth. It told Father Louis that he was afraid.

"Afraid? Of what?" he thought. "Afraid of death? But I have dealt with it all my life and I have robbed it of its terrors for those who knew how to die. Is death the only victory of life? Or do we have to defeat life in its own terms? That depends. It depends upon whether sin is ever outside oneself, or always within. Yes, this is a very interesting matter."

He made himself lie quietly without thought for a moment. If, perhaps, he conserved his energy, he might by natural vitality, by pure goodness, defeat the murder that had been dealt him by the desert. He forced himself to relax, and promised that in a little while his head would be clearer, his heart would calm itself, and, moving with infinite caution, he would arise, mount his horse, and go slowly, steadily, cleverly, toward the long evening and come to the canyon where there must be a familiar trickle of water. A cool night with much prayer, a stout will, and tomorrow he would go forward and by the end of the day come to friends who would know how to make poultices and feed him and recover him to the use and enjoyment of many more years of duty, work, and acquired merit.

But the poison worked rapidly, and he felt it charging his mind with throbbing pain that confused him. Shining bars went across his vision behind his eyes like spokes of a great wheel. He was dazzled by their power. When he raised his head they took it with them, rolling and rolling until he fell down again upon the ground where his cheek was cut by little pebbles of gypsum. He tried to say,

"Let me not live for vanity, though, Lord."

Questions now became academic, for he went blind in his inner vision, and lay trembling as the terrible message that had been stricken into him travelled the course of his blood and reached him everywhere within.

Tied to his mesquite tree, Pancho stamped and waited.

Presently Father Louis believed that he awoke.

His mind was working sharply and with what seemed to him exquisite new ease and clarity. He saw all his thoughts as in crystal depths of cold fresh water. He knew he was in the mesquite thicket, and what had happened to him, and he possessed this knowledge with an elated purity such as he had always known in the state of grace, after receiving or administering the sacraments. It was more than mere physical well-being. It was a sense of delivery from the ordinary guilt of his own clay, and the exasperating weight of the world. It was the real meaning of communion with all that lay beyond himself. In such a state truth needed no seeking, and no definition. It was here, within, and it was there, without. It was everywhere. When all was known there could be no astonishment.

He was therefore not astonished now when right before him, lying at ease in the light of the sun, was the snake gazing at him with piercing sweetness. He spoke to it.

"I do not hate you. It is enough that I recognize you."

The snake replied, "That is my damnation."

"Yes," said Father Louis, "for when evil is recognized all other powers move together to defeat it."

"And yet they never do defeat it, do they? How do you explain that?"

"Ah. You and I do not see it in quite the same way. You conceive of the possible death of evil as being one, final end after which only goodness will survive."

"I do."

"That is your vanity. For the fact is that evil must be done to death over and over again, with every act of life. One might even say that this repeated act is a very condition for the survival of life itself. For only by acts of growth can more life be made, and if all evil, all acts of death, were ended once and for all, there would be nothing left for the soul to triumph over in repeated acts of growth."

The snake sighed despondently, and said, "Do you not permit me a comparable purpose and privilege? That is, of triumphing repeatedly over all acts of good, that is, of life, until only I remain?"

"I permit you your established role, but I do not admit the possibility of your triumphing repeatedly over all acts of life. I must point out that historically your premise is untenable."

"And yet I have played a part in every human life."

"Oh, admittedly. We are not discussing the fact that your powers exist; only the fact that they have their limits."

The snake smiled.

"This? From you?" it asked with ironic politeness.

"What do you mean, sir?"

"If my powers have their limits, then how is it that I have killed you? What greater power is there than that?"

Father Louis passed his hand across his face to hide his amusement.

"You have betrayed the weakness of your whole position," he replied, "for it appears to be impossible for you to know that the death of matter is of no importance, except to other matter. The materialist can see only destruction as the logical end of his powers. I, and my brothers, and my children, know that beyond matter lies spirit, and that it is there where answers are found, and truths become commonplace, and such efforts as yours, so restless, so ingenious, so full of torturing vanity, are seen for what they really are."

The snake frowned for a moment, but then shook off its irritation, and said, again with politeness, even with a charm and appeal that Father Louis was the first to admit, "Everyone must do that which his nature dictates."

"There again," said Father Louis with assumed gravity, "there is much behind the formation of that nature which you do not take into account."

"Oh, come, after all, I am a snake, I came from snakes, I do a snake's work, how could I behave like anything else but a snake?"

"The outer form is hardly the point. You can assume any form you choose, I believe?"

The snake hesitated before answering. A gleam of admiration went through its expression, and it marvelled frankly for a moment at the astuteness of Father Louis.

"I must say, even if we are enemies, you force me to admire and like you," it said.

"Thank you," said Father Louis. "Viewed abstractly, you have great and beautiful qualities of your own."

"Do you really think so?"

"Oh, yes, I do. But I must add that they seem to me less important, in the end, than they do to you."

"You can also be very rude, you know."

"I do not think of it in that way," said Father Louis mildly. "Finally, it doesn't matter how things are said or done, it is what things are said or done. For example, I really believe you can do things far more expertly than I can. But when it comes to what things, there I have you."

The snake looked away, far from pleased.

Father Louis resumed, "I can't assume any form, for example, as you can. I remain always what I am, a man, an old man, a dirty old man when water is scarce or I am busy, an old man full of pride and sin and vanity and all the rest of it; but nobody is ever in doubt about what I mean, or about what I think life means, and with all mistakes in style and good form, the garden I scratch keeps growing."

"And I?"

"And you, sometimes you are a snake, and sometimes a whisper, and again, a daydream, a lump in the blood, a sweet face, an ambition, a scheme for making money, a task for an army. Sometimes you can even be a man and disarm everyone entirely who cannot see your heart. But someone there is who always sees. Goodness is often performed without the slightest knowledge of its doing. But evil is always known."

"Yes, I think more people know me than the other thing."

"But don't congratulate yourself upon that," said Father Louis, "for it always means one of your uncountable defeats when you are known."

Father Louis saw that the snake would have to grow angry unless the subject were changed. The snake changed it.

"I wonder," it mused, "why I ever came to you today."

Father Louis shrugged.

"Sooner or later, we would have come together," he said.

"Did you expect me?"

"I have been expecting you all my life; though not exactly in this particular guise. You came to me in my sleep, like an evil dream."

"All I wanted was a little comfort. It was so hot, so dry."

Father Louis smiled in delight.

"You see? For comfort, even you have to appeal to the powers of goodness."

The snake habitually wore a scowling smile and now for a moment the smile disappeared leaving only the scowl. Then with an effort it restored the smile, and said,

"Why did you let me go?"

"I had no weapon."

"You could have stamped upon me."

"I do not believe in killing."

"Yet I am your enemy."

"Yes, you are. But I believe there are greater ways to dispose of you than in revenge."

"You do not have much time left, you know. Just think of all the time you would have left if I had not come to you. If you had seen me and killed me first."

"Yes, I have thought of that. But you speak as though time were my property. It is not. How can I count it? Or know how much of it is my share?"

The snake frowned and looked from side to side evasively. Unwillingly, against its own comfort, it asked,

"Who else can decide your share? Where do you get it? What do you refer to?"

The snake began uneasily to bring its coils together. There was anguish in its movement, slow as it was. It seemed to be obeying desire which was hurtful and yet impossible to deny.

"You do not really want to hear," said Father Louis tenderly.

"Oh, yes, I do, tell me," said the snake, with broken breath, already suffering under the answer it demanded.

Father Louis bent over the snake with compassion. There was torture in the creature, as with glittering sweet power it begged Father Louis to answer.

"Very well, my poor creature," said Father Louis gravely, "I, and all creatures, draw our share of time in this life from God our Father in Heaven."

At these words the snake with the speed of lightning knew convulsion in its dread coils and with mouth wide open and fangs exposed struck again and again at the earth where the dust rose like particles of gold and silver. Father Louis regarded it with pity as its paroxysm of hatred and chagrin spent itself. At last, gasping softly and stretched out in exhaustion, the snake said, sorrowfully,

"And so it was not by my will that you die now?"

"No."

"I was only the means?"

"Only the means."

"Your hour was designated elsewhere?"

Father Louis looked upward. His face was radiant.

"My hour was fixed by our Heavenly Father."

The snake closed its eyes and shuddered reminiscently. Then it said,

"And my hour?"

"You will die in your bodily form by His will."

"I do not want to die."

"But you will live in your quality of evil, by His will."

"You're sure?"

"Yes. But you will live only on earth, no matter what form you assume."

The snake grew pale.

"Oh, no."

"Yes," said Father Louis, as his argument drew to its close, "for there can be no evil in Heaven."

The snake lay with its mouth open, its tongue like a little tongue of fire flickering in despair, its eyes staring without sight. It was vanquished, destroyed, made trivial. Father Louis shook his head over it and wished it might not have suffered. Then he felt his brow where the diamondine lucidity of the past quarter of an hour seemed to be clouding over. His skull was cracking under blows that beat and beat there. How could he feel so ill after feeling so well?

"And now you must excuse me," he said, uncertainly, to the snake, "I have things to do, and actually, I do not feel too well, thank you, if you will just go now," and he looked to see if the snake was leaving, but the snake was already gone.

The battering pains in his head brought Father Louis from vision to consciousness.

"Oh, my God, my God," he said devoutly and with much effort, even with modesty, representing his trouble to Him whose suffering he had dwelt upon so deeply in a lifetime.

He looked around.

The air seemed entirely silent. This was because there was a ringing in his head so bewildering that he could no longer hear the myriad insects at their screaming celebration of the heat.

He saw Pancho tied to the tree.

"No, you must not stay with me," he said, and tried to stand up. He could barely stand, for his legs were weak as paralysis crept into them. And so he crawled across the open place among the thickets until he could hold to his stirrup, haul himself up, and lean with his head on the saddle for a moment.

"You need not die here, tied to a tree," he said. "Let me get my things, and you may go."

He fumbled with the buckles and straps until he was able to haul the saddle off the horse. It fell to the ground. He worked at the bridle until he had freed it enough to pull it off over Pancho's head. The horsehair bridle hung from the thorny tree and trailed in the dust.

"Huya! Huya!" cried Father Louis, waving his hand at Pancho to make him trot away, as he so often had done after unsaddling the horse at the corral in Brownsville. But Pancho simply stood and regarded him.

"Very well, very well, in your own time, then," he said, and went down to his hands and knees, fondling a pouch on the saddle. Out of it into his hands came the objects he wished to hold once more. Holding them to his breast, he crawled back to his fatal shade across the clearing. The sun was almost down.

"*Magnificat anima mea Dominum,*" he murmured while pains like sharp sea-stones pierced him through and through. Even the heavy washing waves of death could not erase entirely from his foundering mind the terrible privilege of knowing in a final hour what saints might have endured. "*Et exultavit spiritus meus in Deo salutari meo,*" he said without knowing he spoke. But he brought a lifetime of prayer with him to death's door; and in a little while it entered there with him.

III

Pancho late the next evening finished finding his way through the brush back to the house of Encarnadino Guerra. The family saw that he was without his saddle and bridle. Guerra and his big sons went searching and though they persevered for days found nothing in that wilderness of repeated clump and glaring shadow and lost sameness. They had to give up. Later that year when surveyors from an expedition of the United States Army came by his place on their way to Brownsville, Guerra told them the news, and asked them to see that it reached the proper authorities, along with the horse Pancho which he hoped they would take with them.

And then one day, eight years afterward, Guerra was on his way to San Ygnacio on the Rio Grande to see his new grandson, born to the household of his oldest boy who now lived there.

Coming into a small clearing in the brush, he found quite by accident what he had looked for long ago. There was not much left, for the desert earth and sky were voracious. Coyotes and blowing sand, vultures and beating sunlight and wind had worked with the years on flesh and leather, French silk, parchment and homespun. Reverently Guerra took up the few bones that had not been scattered, and the few hard things that still stayed by them: the pewter chalice, a rosary of small sea shells, three American silver dollars, the pair of green sun-glasses, and, from a mesquite tree where it hung now off the ground, the horsehair bridle.

When he could, he made the journey to Brownsville bringing the relics of his old friend with him. He found his way to Father Pierre Arnoud.

"How these things speak to us!" said Father Pierre, after hearing the end of the story that had begun eight years before. He looked at Guerra and saw that this was a man who had lost a dear friend, who would understand anything said to him in the name of Father Louis. He added, "I am leaving soon for France. Do you know where that is?"

"Yes. He used to tell us much about it."

Father Pierre was making ready to obey a summons to return home to receive the dignity of bishop of a French diocese.

"I am going there to assume new work," he said. "These things, this sacrifice," he said, indicating what Guerra had brought, "will help me to do it better."

Guerra nodded.

"We will bury him here in the churchyard," continued Father Pierre, "and you must be present. As you were his friend, and have served him so well now, I would like to ask your permission to keep this."

He held up the little string of sea shells.

"Yes," said Guerra, accepting with simplicity the power to dispose.

"I wonder how he died," murmured Father Pierre. "Indians? A heart attack?"

"Not Indians."

"Why not?"

"They would not have let the horse go."

"True. What then?"

Guerra made a gesture with his mouth, putting his lips forward as though he would point to a place far from there and long ago. He saw the clearing in the thorny brush again, and he knew its nature, all of it.

"I think I know."

"How could you possibly?"

"He did not die suddenly."

"No?"

"No. He had time to free his horse."

"Ah."

"If he thought he could have saved himself, he would have come with the horse."

"Undoubtedly."

"But he did not come. He stayed. That means he knew there wasn't any use."

"And so?"

"Where I found him was just like the place where it would happen."

"What would happen?"

With his hand Guerra made in the air a slow, sinuous motion from side to side in an unmistakable imitation.

"No!" said Father Pierre. "A snake?"

Guerra nodded.

"I think so," he said.

Father Pierre shuddered at the nature of that fate, and then presently he kindled at the memory of an old weakness and an old strength.

"Do you know? I will tell you something," he said. "Our dear friend was an old man, tired, and ill, when he went on that last journey. For days before he left, I was supposed to tell him that he could not go. I tried, and I tried. But I could not tell him. Even on the last morning, I could not give the order."

Father Pierre put his hands together in emotion.

"What could I have saved him from? From dying at his work? That is how we—all of us—want to die, when our time comes."

He looked earnestly at Guerra, but if he thought he would find the abstract pardon of life there, he was mistaken. Guerra simply looked at him with the impersonal judgment of the world.

"No, I could not give the order," resumed Father Pierre. "And do you know? I am sure he knew what I had to say. He would not let me say it. He gave the orders. Just to prove it, he even sent me upstairs to find his green sun-glasses. I went, and I did not find them. When I came down again, there they were, he had them all the time."

Guerra laughed out loud at the crankiness this recalled, and what it meant. He bent over, took up the pair of green-glass spectacles with their rusted tin rims, and with a gleam of meaning, handed them to Father Pierre.

"Then keep these also," he said.

"Thank you," said the bishop-elect soberly.

THE OUTSIDER

Phyllis Bottome

While you work all day long in the open air, you do not hear sounds consciously; you draw them in with your breath: the voices of birds, the long murmur of insects, the rustle and splash of falling water. Only when I heard the soft crush of gravel under the sandals of a brother, I would lift my head to greet him; but often I was not conscious of any sound until the chapel bell summoned me into silence. My work absorbed me. My mother often used to say that from my earliest childhood I had had "green hands," so that plants always grew willingly for me.

All the vines in our great vineyards were under my care. They ran down, in terraces, from the mountain top, and in the hard winters they were on my mind as a sleeping baby is on his mother's mind. The snow lay heavy upon us for four months out of the year, nor had we the certainty of great heat in summer, as they have in Southern lands.

It was not my business to answer the visitor's bell; but one morning in July, I think it was in the second year of my novitiate, I had been told to do this service for Father Thomas, who was wanted elsewhere.

I was a little anxious, for I had had no dealings with visitors since I entered the Kloster, but I thought, "No one will ring the bell this morning. The peasants come in without ringing, and it is too early for pilgrims."

When the bell rang, I hurried down the hillside, knowing that it must be a stranger.

He stood in the gateway, with his bare head shining like kingcups, and a rucksack on his back. His spine, his head, and his heels made one straight line together, without rigidity.

I looked once at him; and then I turned my eyes away from his face; but it was no use. I knew that I should always see him.

I do not know that monks are uglier than other men; as they grow older, if they are true children of God, there is a beauty to be found in all their faces; but it has to be looked for. The beauty of this stranger could not be avoided; it was shattering. Nor was it only the shape and color of his features, or the depths of his eyes (the color of them I never knew), but in the whole person there was no contradiction. He was all beauty, as the sun is all light.

I have been in the Kloster since I was seventeen, and though I have not seen much of the outside world, I have seen many pilgrims; but pilgrims are seldom beautiful, and one is so busy attending to their needs that one is not disturbed by anything they look like; and though the intentions of a pilgrim are good, his manners are rarely attractive. This man was a prince among men.

To make Tokay you take only perfect grapes. He was of that vintage.

In the years that followed I often tried to recall that first meeting, but I could only remember the sun burning upon the apricots.

He asked to see our Father Superior, though it was not the hour for visitors; and I was rebuked because I forgot this, and took him at once to see our Reverend Father.

I went back into the garden to dig as I had been digging when he rang the bell; and it was then that I noticed how sharp and clear were the light summer sounds. The birds' songs penetrated my heart; and the whole valley beneath me sent up a kind of music.

I did not confess this change in me, because I had no wishes; and to this day I think that to love without a wish is not a sin.

Our guest did not stay very long with us, nor did he speak to me.

I saw him sometimes at sunset, or in the early mornings

before the first Mass, standing on the topmost peak of our mountain, under a group of silver birches close to where our monks are buried. We have a very small *Friedhof,* and all of us lie, looking towards the east, at the same distance from the other and with the same small carved crucifix of wood.

Beneath where he stood the mountain drops a thousand feet into the valley, and the Danube winds through the blue plains, glittering like the tail of a dragon.

Our stranger looked like the Blessed Michael standing there, with the light of his golden head, and the Dragon at his feet.

Father Theodosius had given him the rooms which were used long ago for the Emperor's yearly retreat, so it was suspected among us that our guest was a member of the royal family, perhaps the son of an archduke. He spoke to none of us but our Father Superior, and not often to him. He may have been under a vow of silence, or doing some penance; it need not have been pride.

He spent much time in the chapel, kneeling erect, as if he were frozen to the floor; and more time still climbing on to the mountains, which rise beyond our special peak, and wandering there alone, for hours.

The others became accustomed to his presence among us; but to me, whenever I saw him, it was as if the moon suddenly rounded a peak and shone out with all her light.

One day, when I was digging a trench between the vines under the study window of our Superior, I heard the stranger's voice.

The words floated out into the air like living things, and I could not stop them by proclaiming my presence, any more than I could have put up my hand to turn back the flight of a bird.

"Father, I want to stay here always," our guest said. "You know my history. The world of today has no use for me; nor does it contain anything that I desire. I love beauty; and to me God is beauty; and here I have found God. I can give myself up to Him in this Kloster, and it may be that in return you can make use of me. I will take any vows! Only let me stay here where for the first time I have found a beauty which is untravestied!"

There was a silence that seemed longer than the pause between the beats of my heart.

Then our Father Theodosius said: "My dear son, you have said that you love beauty, and that by beauty you mean God. That you win pleasure from this faith I can well believe, but such pleasure is not love."

Our guest cried: "What do you mean, Father? Do I not show my love by my content? Why, I need nothing else but beauty. I am her tireless worshiper! I ask only to be allowed to stay upon my knees."

I thought our Father cruel when he spoke again, although his voice was gentle.

"Lovers give," he said. "They are without needs. There is no other way of showing love but service. You could not serve beauty here, my son, for here she is free—she has no need of servants. But below, where beauty is chained, where you have found such ugliness, such great misery, and so many slaveries —you can serve beauty there! Go down again, my son. Fight for what you love; live for it; and when you have fought and lived until the strength in you is vanquished, then you may come back to where beauty need not be fought for, but is open, without penalties, to all who have eyes to see."

There came a great darkness over my mind so that I could no more hear what either of them said, if they said anything.

It was the hour of vespers.

When I reached the chapel, the lights upon the altar were already lit.

It was high summer, but I felt the blood drain out of my body, and my hands and feet grew cold.

I thought that I had wished for nothing, but I must have wished that he should sometimes be visible.

II

The years pass very quickly when you are doing the same thing in the same place.

I had nothing to complain of; the seasons shifted without menace one into the other.

Between me and the sound of the voice there were many summers. Even the winters passed. There is much to fight against here in the winter—cold and sickness; while among the peasants the teeth of poverty are bared.

The little events of life fell muffled upon my heart, as sounds when snow is falling. I can easily understand how life passes into sleep; sleep into death; and death into eternal peace. It is resurrection that I find difficult to understand—and sometimes painful.

He came again. One day in early spring, in the wake of the March kingcups which run down over our vineyards following the line of the melting snows. The lambs, newly born, tried to dance upon the air; they were so active with surprise and so willing to make sure of their unknown powers.

I should have recognized him anywhere, though time had left a thousand marks upon him; and he had been wounded in a great war. He had known and made changes, and he had been betrayed by great disasters. He had overcome defeat and known how small victory can be; but though he looked worn, and as a sword that has been used too often, his beauty burned on in him.

I think he was glad to come back to us. He did not, of course, remember me; but from the hour of his return we became friends.

He spoke now to all of us. He lived with us, and took our vows.

It seemed to the whole community that his ripeness, and world wisdom, gave to our Kloster a fresh lease of life.

Our Father was growing old, and was often silent, as if he had nothing more to say.

Usually when we are reborn to God we choose our own names, but brother Martin did not choose his. Father Theodosius said to him one day: "My son, let us call you Martin. For Martin gave away half his cloak to a beggar, and you have given away half of yours to that poor old beggar, the world; but I do not yet know what you will do with the other half of it."

I felt angry, for surely it was to us and to the service of our rule that Martin was giving the other half of his cloak. Besides, I had hoped that he would be called Michael.

Father Martin was a great preacher. The first year that he became one of us the pilgrims doubled in quantity. The work in August was so heavy upon us that help had to be brought in from outside. We had to buy food for the pilgrims beyond what we could make out of our stores, and they wanted more wine than the vineyards could give; but many souls were brought to God, so that we were thankful.

I do not know how long it was before Father Martin began to talk about a new rule—stricter than ours; but this thing was a great concern to him. Our daily tasks, he said, were too easy and we prayed less than many monks.

In the winter we never got up before five o'clock in the morning, whereas in many Klosters the brothers serve God on their knees in the heart of the night.

"For," Martin often told me, "if we give God only our comfortable moments, we give Him only half of ourselves—and that the weaker half. A man's soul and body in discomfort also belong to God."

But Father Ambrose, who had been long with us, and was much beloved, spoke differently.

"Let God alone," he said. "It is His business to make us more comfortable or more uncomfortable. We need not add anything to our rule, we have not yet followed it perfectly if we are not satisfied with it."

Some of the brothers accepted Father Martin's ideas, as I must confess I always did, for they seemed reasonable, and in spite of the strictness of his life he had time to spare for any fresh duty or act of kindness; and some of our brothers accepted Father Ambrose's opinion. We took this question to heart so greatly that we strove among ourselves as to which rule was best; and anger came among us, so that we looked without pleasure into each other's eyes, and I sometimes thought that we wasted what might have been given more serviceably to God.

At last our Reverend Father, who had grown very old, and almost altogether silent, sent for us all and asked us to vote upon the subject of our rule. He said that he was too old to judge of a new matter, so that he would not vote himself, but that he was willing to carry out faithfully, and with love, whatever the majority of us thought best.

Nevertheless we all begged him for his opinion, for we knew him to be very wise; and he was bound to us by many years of love and obedience.

For a long time he was silent, looking away from us, through a great window that opened over the yellowing vines. It was autumn and the trees were thin, so that you could see through them down into the valley.

At last he said: "My children, you have asked me to tell you if I think an easy or a stern rule more pleasing to God. But how can I—a poor monk like yourselves—tell what is in the mind of God? His laws are open to us to observe; His life is in us; but what is in His mind we cannot know. A fragment of a rainbow cannot tell you where light is born. But though I cannot tell you what God would wish us to do, I have lived a long time with His children, and I have observed that what we love most we do best. Let those, then, who love our old rule best follow it; and let those who wish to live more strictly have our respect and blessing, and harden the rule for themselves as they see fit."

But Father Martin said: "With due submission, Reverend Father, could it not be that strife might come of this, and that those who believe in the stricter rule might look down upon their weaker brothers who prefer the easier rule, while those who prefer the easier rule might resent the greater strictness of their stronger brothers, and feel themselves provoked by it?"

The Reverend Father was silent for so long that we wondered if he slept; but he spoke at last, looking at Martin as if he deeply loved him, and was expecting something in this love to reach beyond agreement or disagreement.

"I think that might very well be so, my dear son, for we are all human, and few have learned that if their aim is to please God solely it is of no account what others do; nor what others think of them for doing differently. But, my son, do you not speak as if strength is more pleasing to God than weakness? But what can we know of this? A lamb is God's handiwork as well as a lion; and He has never told us that He prefers His lions to His lambs.

"Since all we know is that we are in an imperfect world and very worthy of it, through our own imperfections, let us think well over this question of our aim; and, praying God that the issue may be blessed, let us vote each for the rule which he believes will be of most service to our Community. For surely it is in Unity that man must live, and what is best for all is best for each of us." And, having spoken, the Reverend Father sank more deeply still into silence.

But I was in anguish, for after the Reverend Father had spoken I could no longer see my way so plainly as to voting for the new rule.

Ten of our brothers voted for the old rule, with Father Ambrose for their leader; and ten voted for the new rule, with Father Martin as their leader; but I sat with the empty paper before me and Martin's eyes upon my face.

The others when they had voted went out; and after a while Martin too rose, and smiling down upon me, as if he were sure of my support, he went after the rest.

The Reverend Father slept. After a long time he woke, and found me still beside him. "My son," he asked me, "what is on your mind?"

And I said: "Father, I would gladly accept this harder rule. It was in my heart to do so; but since you have spoken I feel a trouble about my aim. I do not know whether I want to please God, or if I want only to please Father Martin."

"My son," Father Theodosius said, "go into the chapel and pray and God will show you whom you most wish to please."

I went into the chapel, and my heart was like a fiery darkness; I felt all the pains of fire, and could see nothing.

I knew that I was between my friend and God, and it seemed to me that I loved my friend most; and that if I failed him, he would punish me with less love; and that God—if I failed God—would not punish me so much because He had not the power. I loved Martin most. I was ashamed when I knew this, and wept bitterly.

The brothers came into Compline, and prayed more earnestly than usual, and stayed longer on their knees; but at last they all left the chapel except Martin. The altar was between us, but I could see how arrowy straight he kneeled, like a knight, to receive the accolade; and though it was twenty years since he was young, his gold and silver hair glistened like the Danube, winding in sunshine, through the distant plains.

I could feel with what passion his prayers beat upon my defenseless heart. It seemed to me that if he had had faith in me, and had left me alone, I should have cleaved to him; but now that I felt the weight of his prayers against me I knew that I must vote for our old rule. If Martin's aim had been to please God solely, he would not have prayed against me; and with the easier rule we should be constraining no one.

We need never prevent our brothers from being stricter than we; but if they chose the new rule they would force us into a strictness our wills had not accepted; and suddenly, although my heart was heavier than lead, there was light in my soul.

I rose from my knees and Martin turned and looked at me. He knew what I was going to do; and in that look his soul left my soul alone, forever.

My feet took me into the vineyards, but my eyes saw nothing; and I stumbled against the wood of old vines and bruised myself; and once I fell into a pit, which I had dug, and lay there wishing it was my grave.

At last I came to the birches, which I have often thought in autumn were like the Holy Ghost; above their white and slender stems their leaves move lightly like gold and silver wings.

From them I looked down into the valley and cursed my life. I asked to have it taken from me; but before nightfall I went back and gave my voice against Martin.

The Reverend Father knew that I had done this thing; but he said nothing.

III

The motions of life went on the same, but the spirit of it had escaped. I noticed nothing that I did and saw nothing that went on about me. I did not even notice that the Reverend Father was failing fast all winter long; nor was I with him when the end came.

I had loved him greatly all my life; but when I heard that he had passed away I was glad. "Martin will have his way now," I thought; and though I knew that Martin could never forgive me for having failed him, yet I was happier because now he could make our rule what he wished.

I had no doubt in my mind that Martin would be made our new Father Superior, though there were some of our brothers who thought Ambrose might be chosen because he had been longer in the Kloster than any of us. But Martin had brought our fame to all the countryside, and to the big towns as well.

He was everywhere beloved for his great sanctity and his golden tongue. In our Kloster, it is the custom for the Father Superior to name in confidence, to the Father Provincial, the most likely of the brothers to take his place; if the Father Provincial is of the same mind, their choice is final; should they differ, the Bishop is asked to give them his aid and counsel; but we knew that in this case the Bishop had not been called in.

I worked all day in my vineyards, for it was a dangerous moment for my vines, and I was spraying them with peroxide of lime against phylloxera. I thought: "This will be a good year. We shall be able to make Tokay, for there will be perfect grapes."

Suddenly I saw one of the novices running across the terrace. "The Father Provincial is here," he told me breathlessly, "and he has sent you this!" And he thrust a letter into my hands, and stood with his head bowed, submissively, as novices should; but he was watching me—as they also do, and should not; so I turned my back upon him, and the western sun flamed against my eyes, making the words turn black.

"My son," I read, "you will take my place, because you could not vote against our rule, although your heart desired to. When you had not yet made up your mind, I knew that it was already made up, for we only feel undecided when we have decided not to change.

"You will rebel against this order, but only those who do not wish for power can safely use it; so use this power, my most beloved son, that you love your brother more for loving God most."

It was from Father Theodosius, written before his death. I had not known that he loved me with any special love. I covered my face with my hands to shut out the words, but they spun in my mind like the wheels of a torture engine, going round and round against raw flesh.

A voice cried out in me: "Martin! Martin! Martin!"

I saw his face as he stood outside the gate when he came to

the Kloster, so proud and young, in its first beauty. He was alive in my heart, with no one thing forgotten, no one grace denied. I think I knew then that he was dead.

He had thrown away the other half of his cloak.

When they told him that I had been chosen as Father Superior, Martin went to his cell and hanged himself.

We had a doctor who loved us greatly, so there was no scandal; besides, Martin had been a prince.

I buried him as close as I could to the rest of us. You will see the grave under the silver birches. He had the sacred earth from Jerusalem sprinkled over it, and the same crucifix that marks the graves of the brothers. He lies only a few feet from us; but there is the wall between, and this I could not alter. He must lie outside the wall.

THE FACE OF EVIL

Frank O'Connor

I could never understand all the old talk about how hard it is to be a saint. I was a saint for quite a bit of my life and I never saw anything hard in it. And when I stopped being a saint, it wasn't because the life was too hard.

I fancy it is the sissies who make it seem like that. We had quite a few of them in our school, fellows whose mothers intended them to be saints and who hadn't the nerve to be anything else. I never enjoyed the society of chaps who wouldn't commit sin for the same reason that they wouldn't dirty their new suits. That was never what sanctity meant to me, and I doubt if it is what it means to other saints. The companions I enjoyed were the tough gang down the road, and I liked going down of an evening and talking with them under the gas lamp about football matches and school, even if they did sometimes say things I wouldn't say myself. I was never one for criticizing; I had enough to do criticizing myself, and I knew they were decent chaps and didn't really mean much harm by the things they said about girls.

No, for me the main attraction of being a saint was the way it always gave you something to do. You could never say you felt time hanging on your hands. It was like having a room of your own to keep tidy; you'd scour it and put everything neatly back in its place, and within an hour or two it was beginning to look as untidy as ever. It was a full-time job that began when you woke and stopped only when you fell asleep.

I would wake in the morning, for instance, and think how nice it was to lie in bed and congratulate myself on not having to get up for another half hour. That was enough. Instantly a sort of alarm-clock would go off in my mind; the mere thought that I could enjoy half an hour's comfort would make me aware of an alternative, and I'd begin an argument with myself. I had a voice in me that was almost the voice of a stranger, the way it nagged and jeered. Sometimes I could almost visualize it, and then it took on the appearance of a fat and sneering teacher I had some years before at school—a man I really hated. I hated that voice. It always began in the same way, smooth and calm and dangerous. I could see the teacher rubbing his fat hands and smirking.

"Don't get alarmed, boy. You're in no hurry. You have another half hour."

"I know well I have another half hour," I would reply, trying to keep my temper. "What harm am I doing? I'm only imagining that I'm down in a submarine. Is there anything wrong in that?"

"Oh, not the least in the world. I'd say there's been a heavy frost. Just the sort of morning when there's ice in the bucket."

"And what has that got to do with it?"

"Nothing, I tell you. Of course, for people like you it's easy enough in the summer months, but the least touch of frost in the air soon makes you feel different. I wouldn't worry trying to keep it up. You haven't the stuff for this sort of life at all."

And gradually my own voice grew weaker as that of my tormentor grew stronger, till all at once I would strip the clothes from off myself and lie in my nightshirt, shivering and muttering: "So I haven't the suff in me, haven't I?" Then I would go downstairs before my parents were awake, strip, and wash in the bucket, ice or no ice, and when Mother came down she would cry in alarm: "Child of grace, what has you up at this hour? Sure, 'tis only half past seven." She almost took it as a reproach to herself, poor woman, and I couldn't tell her the reason, and even if I could have done so, I wouldn't. It was a thing you couldn't talk about to anybody.

Then I went to Mass and enjoyed again the mystery of the streets and lanes in the early morning; the frost which made your feet clatter off the walls at either side of you like falling

masonry, and the different look that everything wore, as
though, like yourself, it was all cold and scrubbed and new. In
the winter the lights would still be burning red in the little
whitewashed cottages, and in the summer their walls were
ablaze with sunshine so that their interiors were dimmed to
shadows. Then there were the different people, all of whom
recognized one another, like Mrs. MacEntee, who used to be a
stewardess on the boats, and Macken, the tall postman; people
who seemed ordinary enough when you met them during the
day but carried something of their mystery with them at Mass,
as though they, too, were reborn.

I can't pretend I was ever very good at school, but even there
it was a help. I might not be clever, but I had always a secret
reserve of strength to call on in the fact that I had what I
wanted, and that besides it I wanted nothing. People fre-
quently gave me things, like fountain pens or pencil-sharpen-
ers, and I would suddenly find myself becoming attached to
them and immediately know I must give them away, and then
feel the richer for it. Even without throwing my weight
around, I could help and protect kids younger than myself
and yet not become involved in their quarrels. Not to become
involved, to remain detached—that was the great thing; to care
for things and for people, yet not to care for them so much
that your happiness became dependent on them.

It was like no other hobby, because you never really got
the better of yourself, and all at once you would suddenly
find yourself reverting to childish attitudes; flaring up in a wax
with some fellow, or sulking when Mother asked you to go for
a message, and then it all came back; the nagging of the infernal alarm-clock, which grew louder with every moment until
it incarnated as a smooth, fat, jeering face.

"Now, that's the first time you've behaved sensibly for
months, boy. That was the right way to behave to your
mother."

"Well, it *was* the right way. Why can't she let me alone once in a while? I only want to read. I suppose I'm entitled to a bit of peace some time?"

"Ah, of course, you are, my dear fellow. Isn't that what I'm saying? Go on with your book! Imagine you're a cowboy, riding to the rescue of a beautiful girl in a cabin in the woods, and let that silly woman go for the messages herself. She probably hasn't long to live anyway, and when she dies you'll be able to do all the weeping you like."

And suddenly tears of exasperation would come to my eyes and I'd heave the story-book to the other side of the room and shout back at the voice that gave me no rest: "Cripes, I might as well be dead and buried. I have no blooming life." After that I would apologize to Mother (who, poor woman, was more embarrassed than anything else and assured me that it was all her fault), go on the message, and write another tick in my notebook against the heading "Bad Temper" so as to be able to confess it to Father O'Regan when I went to Confession on Saturday. Not that he was ever severe with me, no matter what I did; he thought I was the last word in holiness, and was always asking me to pray for some special intention of his own. And though I was depressed, I never lost interest, for no matter what I did, I could scarcely ever reduce the total of times I had to tick off that item in my notebook.

Oh, I don't pretend it was any joke, but it did give me the feeling that my life had some meaning; that inside me I had a real source of strength; that there was nothing I could not do without and yet remain sweet, self-sufficient, and content. Sometimes, too, there was the feeling of something more than mere content, as though my body were transparent, like a window, and light shone through it as well as on it, onto the road, the houses, and the playing children, as though it were I who was shining on them, and tears of happiness would come into my eyes, and I hurled myself among the playing children just to forget it.

But, as I say, I had no inclination to mix with other kids who might be saints as well. The fellow who really fascinated

me was a policeman's son named Dalton, who was easily the
most vicious kid in the locality. The Daltons lived on the
terrace above ours. Mrs. Dalton was dead; there was a younger
brother called Stevie who was next door to an imbecile, and
there was something about that kid's cheerful grin that was
even more frightening than the malice on Charlie's broad face.
Their father was a tall melancholy man with a big black
mustache, and the nearest thing imaginable to one of the Key-
stone cops. Everyone was sorry for his loss in his wife, but you
knew that if it hadn't been that, it would have been something
else—maybe the fact that he hadn't lost her. Charlie was only
an additional grief. He was always getting into trouble, stealing and running away from home; and only his father's being
a policeman prevented his being sent to an industrial school.
One of my most vivid recollections is that of Charlie's education. I'd hear a shriek, and there would be Mr. Dalton dragging Charlie along on the pavement to school and, whenever
the names his son called him grew a little more obscene than
usual, pausing to give Charlie a good going-over with the belt
which he carried loose in his hand. It is an exceptional father
who can do this without getting some pleasure out of it, but
Mr. Dalton looked as though even it were an additional
burden. Charlie's screams could always fetch me out.

"What is it?" Mother would cry after me.

"Ah, nothing. Only Charlie Dalton again."

"Come in! Come in!"

"I won't be seen."

"Come in, I say. 'Tis never right."

And even when Charlie uttered the most atrocious in-
decencies, she only joined her hands as if in prayer and
muttered, "The poor child! The poor unfortunate child!" I
never could understand the way she felt about Charlie. He
wouldn't have been Charlie if it hadn't been for the leatherings and the threats of the industrial school.

Looking back on it, the funniest thing is that I seemed to
be the only fellow on the road he didn't hate. They were all

terrified of him, and some of the kids would go a mile to avoid him. He was completely unclassed: being a policeman's son, he should have been way up the social scale, but he hated the respectable kids worse than the others. When we stood under the gas lamp at night and saw him coming up the road, everybody fell silent. He looked suspiciously at the group, ready to spring at anyone's throat if he saw the shadow of offence; ready even when there wasn't a shadow. He fought like an animal, by instinct, without judgment, and without ever reckoning the odds, and he was terribly strong. He wasn't clever; several of the older chaps could beat him to a frazzle when it was merely a question of boxing or wrestling, but it was never that with Dalton. He was out for blood and usually got it. Yet he was never that way with me. We weren't friends. All that ever happened when we passed each other was that I smiled at him and got a cold, cagey nod in return. Sometimes we stopped and exchanged a few words, but it was an ordeal because we never had anything to say to each other.

It was like the signalling of ships, or, more accurately, the courtesies of great powers. I tried, like Mother, to be sorry for him in having no proper home, and getting all those leatherings, but the feeling that came uppermost in me was never pity but respect—respect for a fellow who had done all the things I would never do: stolen money, stolen bicycles, run away from home, slept with tramps and criminals in barns and dosshouses, and ridden with a ticket on trains and on buses. It filled my imagination. I have a vivid recollection of one summer morning when I was going up the hill to Mass. Just as I reached the top and saw the low, sandstone church perched high up ahead of me, he poked his bare head around the corner of a lane to see who was coming. It startled me. He was standing with his back to the gable of a house; his face was dirty and strained; it was broad and lined, and the eyes were very small, furtive and flickering, and sometimes a sort of spasm would come over them and they flickered madly for half a minute on end.

"Hullo, Charlie," I said. "Where were you?"

"Out," he replied shortly.

"All night?" I asked in astonishment.

"Yeh," he replied in a nod.

"What are you doing now?"

He gave a short, bitter laugh.

"Waiting till my old bastard of a father goes out to work and I can go home."

His eyes flickered again, and self-consciously he drew his hand across them as though pretending they were tired.

"I'll be late for Mass," I said uneasily. "So long."

"So long."

That was all, but all the time at Mass, among the flowers and the candles, watching the beautiful, sad old face of Mrs. MacEntee and the plump, smooth handsome face of Macken, the postman, I was haunted by the image of that other face, wild and furtive and dirty, peering round a corner like an animal looking from its burrow. When I came out, the morning was brilliant over the valley below me; the air was punctuated with bugle calls from the cliff where the barrack stood, and Charlie Dalton was gone. No, it wasn't pity I felt for him. It wasn't even respect. It was almost like envy.

Then, one Saturday evening, an incident occurred which changed my attitude to him; indeed, changed my attitude to myself, though it wasn't until long after that I realized it. I was on my way to Confession, preparatory to Communion next morning. I always went to Confession at the parish church in town where Father O'Regan was. As I passed the tramway terminus at the Cross, I saw Charlie sitting on the low wall above the Protestant church, furtively smoking the butt-end of a cigarette which somebody had dropped, getting on the tram. Another tram arrived as I reached the Cross, and a number of people alighted and went off in different directions. I crossed the road to Charlie and he gave me his most distant nod.

"Hullo."

"Hullo, Cha. Waiting for somebody?"

"No. Where are you off to?"

"Confession."

"Huh." He inhaled the cigarette butt deeply and then tossed it over his shoulder into the sunken road beneath without looking where it alighted. "You go a lot."

"Every week," I said modestly.

"Jesus!" he said with a short laugh. "I wasn't there for twelve months."

I shrugged my shoulders. As I say, I never went in much for criticizing others, and anyway Charlie wouldn't have been Charlie if he had gone to Confession every week.

"Why do you go so often?" he asked challengingly.

"Oh, I don't know," I said doubtfully. "I suppose it keeps you out of harm's way."

"But you don't do any harm," he growled, just as though he were defending me against someone who had been attacking me.

"Ah, we all do harm."

"But, Jesus Christ, you don't do anything," he said almost angrily, and his eyes flickered again in that curious nervous spasm, and almost as if they put him into a rage, he drove his knuckles into them.

"We all do things," I said. "Different things."

"Well, what do you do?"

"I lose my temper a lot," I admitted.

"Jesus!" he said again, and rolled his eyes.

"It's a sin just the same," I said obstinately.

"A sin? Losing your temper? Jesus, I want to kill people. I want to kill my bloody old father, for one. I will too, one of those days. Take a knife to him."

"I know, I know," I said, at a loss to explain what I meant. "But that's just the same thing as me."

I wished to God that I could talk better. It wasn't any missionary zeal. I was excited because for the first time I knew that Charlie felt about me exactly as I felt about him, with a sort of envy, and I wanted to explain to him that he didn't have to envy me, and that he could be as much a saint as I was just as I could be as much a sinner as he was. I wanted to explain that it wasn't a matter of tuppence ha-penny worth of sanctity as opposed to tuppence worth that made the difference, that it wasn't what you did but what you lost by doing it that mattered. The whole Cross had become a place of mystery—the grey light, drained of warmth; the trees hanging over the old crumbling walls; the tram, shaking like a boat when someone mounted it. It was the way I sometimes felt afterwards with a girl, as though everything about you melted and fused and became one with a central mystery.

"But what you do isn't any harm!" he repeated angrily with that flickering look of the eyes I had almost come to dread.

"Look, Cha," I said, "you can't say a thing isn't any harm. Everything is harm. It might be losing my temper with me and murder with you, like you say, but it would only come to the same thing. If I show you something, will you promise not to tell?"

"Why would I tell?"

"But promise."

"Oh, all right."

Then I took out my little notebook and showed it to him. It was extraordinary, and I knew it was extraordinary. I found myself, sitting on that wall, showing a notebook I wouldn't have shown to anyone else in the world to Charlie Dalton, a fellow any kid on the road would go a long way to avoid, and yet I had the feeling that he would understand it as no one else would do. My whole life was there, under different headings—Disobedience, Bad Temper, Bad Thoughts, Selfishness, and Laziness—and he looked through it quietly, studying the ticks I had placed against each count.

"You see," I said, "you talk about your father, but look at all the things I do against my mother. I know she's a good mother, but if she's sick or if she can't walk fast when I'm in town with her, I get mad just as you do. It doesn't matter what sort of mother or father you have. It's what you do to yourself when you do things like that."

"What do you do to yourself?" he asked quietly.

"It's hard to explain. It's only a sort of peace you have inside yourself. And you can't be just good, no matter how hard you try. You can only do your best, and if you do your best you feel peaceful inside. It's like when I miss Mass of a morning. Things mightn't be any harder on me that day than any other day, but I'm not as well able to stand up to them. It makes things a bit different for the rest of the day. You don't mind it so much if you get a hammering. You know there's something else in the world besides the hammering."

I knew it was a feeble description of what morning Mass really meant to me, the feeling of strangeness which lasted throughout the whole day and reduced reality to its real proportions, but it was the best I could do. I hated leaving him.

"I'll be late for Confession," I said regretfully, getting off the wall.

"I'll go down a bit of the way with you," he said, giving a last glance at my notebook and handing it back to me. I knew he was being tempted to come to Confession along with me, but my pleasure had nothing to do with that. As I say, I never had any missionary zeal. It was the pleasure of understanding rather than that of conversion.

He came down the steps to the church with me and we went in together.

"I'll wait for you here," he whispered, and sat in one of the back pews.

It was dark there; there were just a couple of small, unshaded lights in the aisles above the confessionals. There was a crowd of old women outside Father O'Regan's box, so I knew I had a long time to wait. Old women never got done with their confessions. For the first time I felt it long, but when my turn came it was all over in a couple of minutes: the usual "Bless you, my child. Say a prayer for me, won't you?" When I came out, I saw Charlie Dalton sitting among the old women out-

side the confessional, waiting to go in. He looked very awkward and angry, his legs wide and his hands hanging between
them. I felt very happy about it in a quiet way, and when I
said my penance I said a special prayer for him.

It struck me that he was a long time inside, and I began to
grow worried. Then he came out, and I saw by his face that it
was no good. It was the expression of someone who is
saying to himself with a sort of evil triumph: "There, I told you
what it was like."

"It's all right," he whispered, giving his belt a hitch. "You
go home."

"I'll wait for you," I said.

"I'll be a good while."

I knew then Father O'Regan had given him a heavy penance,
and my heart sank.

"It doesn't matter," I said. "I'll wait."

And it was only long afterwards that it occurred to me that I
might have taken one of the major decisions of my life without
being aware of it. I sat at the back of the church in the dusk
and waited for him. He was kneeling up in front, before the
altar, and I knew it was no good. At first I was too stunned to
feel. All I knew was that my happiness had all gone. I admired
Father O'Regan; I knew that Charlie must have done things
that I couldn't even imagine—terrible things—but the resentment grew in me. What right had Father O'Regan or anyone to
treat him like that? Because he was down, people couldn't help
wanting to crush him further. For the first time in my life I
knew real temptation. I wanted to go with Charlie and share
his fate. For the first time I realized that the life before me
would have complexities of emotion which I couldn't even
imagine.

The following week he ran away from home again, took a
bicycle, broke into a shop to steal cigarettes, and, after being
arrested seventy-five miles from Cork in a little village on the
coast, was sent to an industrial school.

I, SAID THE SPARROW

Arthur J. Roth

Before I start this story of how a boyhood friend lost his eye, I have to tell you about "convoys." When I recently went home to Ireland, after an eighteen-year absence, I was sure that the "convoy"—like thruppenny chunks of Yellow Man candy, the big Turkey Market in November, and the Sunday pitch-and-toss school behind the ball alley—had been long ago unceremoniously banished among the quaint rituals of social history by the members of a younger generation that, not content with just *embracing* the twentieth century, had it already half digested and were reaching for whatever tidbits they could glimpse of the twenty-first. The young crowd now, true Europeans to a man, thought nothing of hiking through France or Italy on their holidays, or even setting off on a two-week boat, rail and plane tour of Lapland; whereas in *my* time vacation had been a three-hour crawling train journey to Bundoran in County Donegal, all of forty miles away, to confront what seemed to us to be the greatest natural wonder in the world: a grey and brawling Atlantic that periodically took a chest-heaving breath and sent its cavalry charging into the cliffs—great sullen brutes of waves that looked as if they'd leap Donegal itself and land far back in County Tyrone. Watching the breakers explode into fifty-foot columns of spray, it was easy then to believe in Saint Patrick's dying wish: that Ireland be immersed beneath the seas a year before the rest of the world went up in flames, a legend that was supposed to be comforting, though I don't know why, remembering those waves.

But getting back to convoys, they'd been a regular thing in the past. Even in 1945, the year I left, you still heard of one every now and again. They were widely held back in the last century, when every Irish railway station had its convoy morning, and again in the decade after World War I, when another big wave of emigrants went over.

A convoy was simply a party for someone who was emigrating, a party that started in the late evening and went on all night and into the morning, with singing and dancing and relays in the kitchen of "a little cup of tay and a bite in your hand." When morning came the hardiest souls, along with the emigrant and his family, would troop to the railway station to wave a red-eyed exile off on the nine-fifteen to Derry City. There he caught the tender out of Moville and transferred to the Cunard Liner anchored at the mouth of Lough Foyle. Back in the twenties Friday had been convoy day in my town and it was common then to find a dozen emigrants at the railway station, surrounded by their families and late revellers. But times have changed. The transatlantic liners no longer call at Derry City, and emigrants now leave from Shannon Airport on great silvery jets that bear the exotic shields of a score of different nations.

Convoys used to be charged with the same sort of gay melancholy that infuses a good wake, which in effect they really were, as in times gone past most of the immigrants never returned. I suppose it's this business of returning that holds the key to the gradual disappearance of convoys. It's hard to get all worked up over a fellow who's liable to pop back in the summer on a twenty-one-day jet excursion fare.

Anyway, I had been home almost a month when one evening my twenty-year-old cousin Sean, the milking all done, came into the kitchen, rubbed his hands together and asked me how I'd like to go to a convoy that evening. Teezie Devlin, of the Mullinaslin Devlins, was emigrating to Philadelphia.

A couple of hours later I found myself, along with Sean and his sister Bella, squeezed into the front of Sean's Austin van, bouncing along a sunken lane that cut through a patch of rough mountain pasturage. Whin bushes, crowned with tiny yellow blossoms, towered on either side of us and only when we came rising over a hump was it possible to see the surrounding land. Although it was ten-thirty there was still plenty of light. It was mid-July and in our part of Ireland—which is roughly the same latitude as northern Labrador—we get those long, almost arctic, twilights. With the bouncing of the van it was impossible to make conversation and we braced our jiggling bodies as best we could while Sean, with a casual one-handed expertise that was largely for the benefit of his "poor wee cousin from Yankeeland," guided the vehicle along until we breasted through Mullinaslin Gap and went flying down a long straight hill. At the bottom Sean spun the wheel in a sharp right turn and we headed straight for a pair of large stone pillars. I grabbed the door handle. We shot through the open space with all of an inch to spare and came to a wheel-locking, pebble-scattering stop in the middle of a large farmyard.

Already half a dozen assorted cars and vans were parked in the yard, plus three motorcycles, a scooter and a few bikes. In my time it would have been *all* bicycles, twenty or thirty of them, with maybe a pony and trap or two.

We entered the kitchen to be introduced around, whereupon I was immediately captured by old Mrs. Devlin, the only one to be wearing a shawl I noticed, and in no time at all she had Teezie and me off in a corner and for the next half hour, a bottle of stout in my hand, I held forth on the assorted pitfalls and promises of Philadelphia, a city I had visited only once, for twenty minutes or so, driving through on my way to Washington. At one point I was about to make my escape when Mrs. Devlin heard from Sean that I was a high school teacher, a fact that set her off on another round of exclamations. She stepped back and eyed me with a new respect. "Did you hear that, Teezie? A high school teacher!" She clapped her hands, everybody seemed to be clapping their hands at me that evening, and exclaimed, "Ah God love him, hadn't he got on well? And sure when he left here he was just a wee lad running around with his stockings at half-mast and a drop at the end of his nose that would drown a kitten." Which wasn't the image I had of myself at all. In retrospect, it seems to me that I had been one hell of a man with the women and all thunder and lightning on the football field. Be that as it may, I finally got out of the kitchen, and went out to the yard where I stood for a moment, nostalgia weighing me down as I looked around at the familiar shapes of my childhood; the byre, the creamery cans, the big square doughal, even the pointed twin white pillars that marked the entrance to every farmyard in the North of Ireland.

Of course the pillars had long since lost their innocence; a college professor having taught me to recognize *those* particular shapes as phallic symbols, hangovers from a Celtic past, erected (forgive the pun) to propitiate the goddess of fertility or some similar esoteric prompting. Yet looking at them, I suddenly realized that they had been built round and smooth like that to eliminate any sharp edges that might catch the side of a cow and cause harm. There's a sort of Murphy's Law for cattle also: if two cows can get jammed in a gap, they will. The reason for the dunce cap hoods that crowned each pillar was equally plain and practical. Internal moisture was the great enemy of anything built with lime-mortar, and what better shape for shedding rain and snow than a cone? For a moment I was twelve years back in the past, taking a course entitled "Primitive Peoples of Western Europe," listening to Professor Burckhardt explain the significance of those particular shapes. I saw myself rise to my feet and softly state, "I beg to take issue with you on that point, Professor, but it so happens that those pillars are constructed in such a fashion because . . . ," and on to jamming cows and lime-mortar. Yield Burckhardt, I've got your number. How I would have relished that moment. I had a natural hatred of anyone who could possibly consider the Irish a primitive people, not to mention the Scots, the Welsh, the Bretons and the Basques.

Leaving Burckhardt vanquished there in the dust of the farmyard, I turned away and began to track the sound of an accordion; followed it up an outside flight of stone steps, ducked my head to clear the low lintel beam of the doorway, and entered a noisy and crowded hayloft. Making my way along the wall, I sat down on one of the benches and looked around. The stone walls had been newly whitewashed and, considering that the place was actually a barn, the floor was in pretty decent shape, having been specially made smooth for the night's dancing by the liberal application of Lux soap flakes, little drifts of which could be seen in the corners and along the walls, swept there in the drafts kicked up by trouser cuffs and belling skirts. Up through the open rafters overhead I could see resting a horse's complete yock—collar, hames, britch-ings and bridle—and I wondered at the equipment being stored in such an awkward place merely to clear the loft for a one-night dance. Then I noticed the coating of dust on the leather and remembered the yellow Fordson tractor, parked in the little orchard behind the house.

There must have been thirty couples on the floor, doing a set, and the exuberant way they went about it caused the planks beneath my feet to set up their own creaking rhythm. I glanced over at the band; there were four musicians, sweat glistening their foreheads as one bellowsed the accordion, two sawed away on fiddles and the fourth punished his drum. With a queer little start I noticed that one of the fiddlers was Poke McAleer. There was a time when Poke and I were inseparable.

The dance ended and Sean came over and sank down beside me, half panting still from the strenuous demands of the six-hand reel. "Are you not dancing?" he finally asked.

"I just came in."

"I see your old friend Jimmy Grimes is here."

"Oh, yes?" I looked around and sure enough there he was in a corner, surrounded by half a dozen younger fellows.

"Blathering away as usual," Sean said, trying to get a rise out of me.

"Right enough, Jimmy was always a great one for talk."

"Aye, and other things," Sean said darkly.

The little group shifted and I had a good look at Jimmy. The passage of time had worn some fairly deep ruts. Though still only thirty-seven, he had the face of a man in his late forties; that great square jaw of his had grown wattles; his upper cheeks wore the permanent flush of a heavy drinker, while the lower jaws curved in, revealing all too plainly that most of his back teeth had fallen by the wayside. The eyes looked the same, though I knew if I got a bit closer they'd likely be bloodshot from the succession of wee nips he'd undoubtedly downed earlier in the evening. Then once more I looked over at the band, at Poke McAleer running a cube of rosin up and down one of the fiddle strings. Even with the collapsed eyelid Poke looked ten years younger, the face still sharp and unseamed, the forehead smooth. Yet all three of us were the same age. This was my first look at Poke since I'd been back, though I'd caught a glimpse of Jimmy before, from a distance, sloping into McCarran's entry after hours one evening, on the prowl for another thirsty diehard like himself.

As luck would have it, Jimmy noticed me at that moment and came up the hall, a big smile on his face. Watching him, you'd swear the man was stone sober but I knew my Jimmy of old.

"So you're back?"

"I am indeed, Jimmy."

"By God," he exclaimed in that boisterous way of his, "you're looking well. The States must agree with you."

"You're not much changed yourself, Jimmy."

"I'm not, that's a fact. I'm still at the dances every week." He leaned closer, bathing me in whisky fumes as he whispered, "But sure the women are a lot smarter nowadays."

Which meant, I knew, that he didn't have his pick and choice anymore.

He pinched my arm. "Listen, I've a bottle in the car below, you'll give me a hand with it?"

"I'd rather not, Jimmy," I lied easily. "I had a few early on and they didn't sit too well."

He was mountainously offended. "What do you mean? Hell to your soul, wasn't it *me* that taught you to drink?"

Couples were moving out to the floor to take their places for a set and I glanced around for someone I could say I had promised the dance to. Most of the girls were unknown to me and Bella already had a partner.

"We'll just slip out for a minute," Jimmy urged, pulling at my arm.

I let myself be persuaded and we edged through the forming groups of dancers, went out the door and clattered down the stairs. I followed him across the cobblestoned yard to his car, an old Morris Eight with the back cut away to form a cargo bed. He clambered in front, shouting instructions, "Go you around and get in the other side. Mind the door, it's a bit balky."

I got in and closed—as best I could—the badly sprung door.

Face turned sideways and head resting against the steering wheel, one hand down between his thighs, Jimmy was rummaging away in the interior of the front seat. He closed his eyes and I wondered if he had fallen asleep, but a final shoulder-wrenching squirm and he pulled out a half full bottle of Old Bushmills.

"Have to hide it," he grunted. "There's a bunch of wee snots running around to the dances now that'd steal you blind."

He offered the bottle and I pulled out the cork and took a token swallow.

"America must have ruined your thirst," he said, noticing how little I'd had. "Go on man, have a decent drink. Sure I'm not charging for it."

I swallowed another mouthful and handed the bottle back. He rested it on the steering wheel and stared out through the windshield at the gable of the house. "Did you see him?"

"I did."

"He can play the fiddle, can't he?"

"He plays well."

"I'm not codding you, he's a genius with the bloody thing."

He lifted his arm and began worrying the neck of the bottle.

"You're not married yet, Jimmy," I said, trying to change the subject.

"No more than yourself."

"Sure we've plenty of time yet."

He wiped his mouth with the back of his hand and said bitterly, "Ach, I should have left this bleeding kip when you did. You're well out of it."

"It's not a bad wee spot all the same, I've often been home-sick for it."

With a drunken change of mood, he brought one hand down on my shoulder and gave an affectionate squeeze. "God be with the old days. We had some smashing times, didn't we?"

"That we did, Jimmy."

"Will you ever forget the night the three of us took off for a dance in Altmore with one bicycle, and us blind to the gills."

I fell in with his mood. "With me on the bar and you pedalling and Poke trotting alongside."

"It was like a bloody dance so it was, the three of us changing partners every turn of the road."

"When we weren't pulling the bicycle out of the ditch."

"The three must-get-theirs, we were a holy terror weren't we?"

"We were, I suppose."

"Have you talked to him at all?"

"Not yet."

"He's changed a lot."

I said nothing and like an old recurring nightmare the scene came back to me, Poke on his knees in the snow, his hands covering his face, and screaming in a voice that made both Jimmy and me want to take to our heels.

Up till then we'd been bosom buddies, the three of us. Jimmy had been the ringleader and both Poke and I would have followed him anywhere. That was the sort of personality Jimmy had. There wasn't an ounce of fear in his body, he was a natural football player, and a charmer with women; three qualities that Poke and I admired extravagantly. We closed our eyes to the touch of tyrant in him and like two flatterers fought for his favor. And Jimmy took advantage of it, he was forever setting one of us against the other, although never to the point where we three broke up. He was good at pouring oil when it suited him. I suppose that sort of adolescent friendship with its fanatic, almost feminine, underground of passion and intrigue had to fade away eventually. Indeed, it was probably fading already that winter of the blizzard but the accident finished everything.

That winter is still called in Dungarvan the year of the big snow. In fact the town had been completely cut off for three days, that being part of the whole misfortune too, for the accident happened the first afternoon of the snow. Earlier, Jimmy and I had been fooling around on the Square, kicking at the quarter-inch of snow that had already accumulated. With a bit of scraping, there was just enough to pack into a snowball and we fired an experimental few at the hanging sign that marked the northwest corner of the Square, "C. Lagan, Licensed to Sell Beer, Wine and Spirits to be Consumed on or off the Premises." We decided the snow wasn't deep enough yet for really effective work, so we went over to Foyle's and talked to Old Hughey for a while. Half an hour later we checked the snow again, pronounced it in fine shape, and went to look for Poke to see what mischief the three of us could invoke. As luck would have it, we turned the corner of the Square and there, about twenty yards ahead, in the middle of the road and with his back to us, stood the bold Poke, looking up at Brophy's second-story window. Breege had the curtains half parted and was staring down at him. I don't know but Poke might have been considering the idea of letting fly with a snowball to throw a bit of a fright into Breege, not too much of a fright because we all knew that Jimmy was a bit taken with her. You might say she was his current girl friend, although current usually meant a month at the most with Jimmy. Naturally Poke and I hated her.

Anyway, we stood there for a moment, the four of us, Jimmy and I with a snowball apiece in our hands; Poke, his back to us, staring up at the face framed between the two curtain halves; and Breege looking over Poke's head and down to where we stood, a few yards behind him. This whole scene has to be visualized through a veil of drifting snow, fine white powdery granules, a pointillist effect you might say.

Then Jimmy said something like, "I'll shout at him and when he turns around we'll both let fly." Just then Breege motioned to Poke with her hand, stabbing her forefinger back and forth as though to say, "There, behind you see?", either in an attempt to warn him of our intentions, or in the hope that he would turn around and present a more enticing target for her boy friend to aim at. To this day I don't know what made him turn, Breege's warning, or Jimmy's shout, or some sixth sense of his own, but turn he did and caught a snowball between the eyes and one on the chest. He fell to his knees in the middle of the road and I, for one, naturally assumed he did so in order to retaliate, to get closer to the ammunition. But, his hands up and covering his face, he began to scream, rocking himself back and forth.

There'd been a piece of sharp pointed gravel in one of the snowballs and it had pierced his left eye. I ran down for Doctor Fitzgerald while Jimmy stayed behind, but the Doctor was out on a call. I left a message with the housekeeper and then went to Sheehy's. Mrs. Sheehy had been a nurse before she married Tom. I told her what had happened and she threw on a coat and came hurrying up the street. I meant to go back and see how Poke was, but the memory of him screaming, rocking his body back and forth in the snow, was too terrifying to face so I sneaked in the back way of our place and hid in my room.

It almost seems as though Poke was fated to lose that eye. Doctor Fitzgerald didn't get back until eight that night—he'd run into trouble with the state of the roads. By then over a foot of snow had fallen, a fine, dry and powdery snow that was drifting as high as three and four feet in places. Doctor Fitzgerald did what he could but it snowed all that night and half the next day and it was yet another day before the roads were clear again. By the time they got Poke to a hospital there was no hope anymore of saving the eye.

Later we made it up, Jimmy and I, to say that we didn't know whose snowball it was that hit Poke in the face. Actually mine hadn't, I'm sure I would have felt the stone when I was making the snowball, but maybe Jimmy thought the same.

Psychologists claim we tend to repress unhappy memories but it hasn't worked out that way for me. Periodically now for eighteen years I have seen two snowballs winging through the flake-filled air, one a little above and a little behind the other, both of them converging on the dark blur of a head in motion. For eighteen years I've willed both snowballs to collide and break into harmless fragments, but for eighteen years they've missed each other and continued true to their target. I see one of them hit Poke in the face and sense the other breaking on his chest. It isn't that I see the one that did the damage more clearly because I am following the flight of my *own* snowball, it's simply that the one that struck him in the face had the more dramatic impact. It hit the bridge of his nose, clung there for a second, then slowly broke apart and fell in two halves.

In my countless re-creations of the scene I must admit that— when we turn the corner and see Poke staring up at Breege—I have often detected a violent flush of jealousy on Jimmy's face as he bent to knead the snow. But it wasn't like that at all. Jimmy's suggestion that we snowball Poke seemed the most natural thing in the world, the same thought had crossed my own mind. At other times I have even, illogical as it sounds, somehow succeeded in summoning an ambulance, an American one oddly enough, which I send forth on a journey down through the years to emerge on our street and make its way, slowly but doggedly, rear wheels spinning, up to where the consoling Jimmy and wounded Poke are kneeling in the snow.

Sometimes I am sitting beside the driver, urging him on, while other times I am behind the vehicle, pushing. But in all my re-shufflings of that scene, I cannot make those two snowballs collide and fall harmlessly to the ground; no matter how I bend their trajectories, one always whispers past the other to strike home.

So there you are, I can't help feeling that a quarter-inch piece of gravel changed all our lives. I emigrated about a year after Poke lost his eye and though I had a dozen good reasons for leaving Dungarvan, I often wonder if the sight of that sunken, somehow accusing, eyelid wasn't the real cause of my flight. I can remember all too clearly my irritation at Poke for not wearing the glass eye that the hospital had furnished. As for Jimmy, he never prospered after that. The youthful drinking sprees grew longer and longer, became inspired less by spontaneous acts of joy and more by the grimly predictable and ordinary happenings of everyday life. He's let the old Grimes farm go to rack and ruin, blackberry bushes all over the fields, gaps in all the hedges. It's only a matter of time before he loses the place.

And Poke? Surely he would never have taken up music and fishing, those two somehow solitary pastimes that became such a part of his life after losing the eye. I *hate* that phrase. It sounds as though he absent-mindedly misplaced the eye, set it for a moment in an old can of screws and nails out in the barn and then forgot where he put it. Anyway, before the accident, I don't think Poke had ever had a fiddle in his hands, although he did go, like the rest of us, to Lough Bracken every once in a while to try for a pike.

Before I tell you what happened to Breege let me finish with the convoy. I finally managed to get away from Jimmy and make my way back to the dance. As it turned out the band was having a break. It's usually the custom to leave behind one man to play for the crowd until the rest of the band comes back, an accordionist or fiddler who runs through a medley of old tried and true numbers with every now and then a modern hit thrown in. I remember, for example, how incongruous "Oh, Mein Papa" sounded that night, its typically teary and German sentimentality completely out of place among the lilting drives of jig, reel and hornpipe.

I went up and joined the crowd that had formed around the makeshift platform where Poke, the stay-behind man, was playing one of those old Irish airs on his fiddle, "The Rakes of Mallow" or "The Sweets of May." He was really making the instrument sing, throwing back his head and lifting the fiddle as he reached for a high note, then bending low to croon at the bridge. I noticed, of course, that he stood sideways, presenting his good profile, but as I watched the oblivious ecstasy on his face and in his movements, I thought that of all of us he had come out of the incident the best. I sensed, with a sort of sad, tumbling-into-middle-age feeling, that never would I get out of teaching, or Jimmy get out of the bottle, what Poke got out of his fiddle. But then again, maybe that's what I *wanted* to think.

With a quivering, sawing-down movement of the bow he brought the piece to an end. A round of clapping broke out; he had carried all of us with him, and he lifted his sweat-drenched face in pleasant surprise, his one eye travelling around the circle of onlookers.

"I heard you were back."

"Back for a visit."

"You'll have to drop over some evening."

"I will surely, Poke," I said, though I had no intention of doing so. I was trying to think of a way to frame a compliment on his playing when the other three musicians came back, dragging on the butt ends of their cigarettes. From the sheepish satisfaction on their faces I knew that they'd been asked down to the kitchen for a few bottles of stout, "to take the edge off their thirst." That's part of the custom too. I took advantage of their return to move away from the platform, ostensibly looking for Sean or Bella. They were both involved with companions and I didn't feel like breaking in on either of them, so I walked outside and went down the steps, intending to see if

I could scrounge another bottle of porter in the kitchen. As I crossed the yard I passed Jimmy's odd-looking wagon and noticed him slumped inside, his folded arms laid over the steering wheel, his head down and fast asleep. I was tempted to wake him, changed my mind and headed for the front door of the farmhouse. Just before I entered I heard the band start up again.

And that's all that happened at the convoy, which brings me now to Breege and here I have to be careful. You see the trouble is that I've told this story before, many times. Once, for example, to a charming old lady I met at a teachers' convention and for *her* I omitted any reference to myself. There's only Poke, Jimmy and Breege, and to give the story a nice, pleasant ending Breege marries Poke and they eventually become the proud parents of four bouncing baby boys. On another occasion, trying to illustrate the Irish sense of guilt for a school psychiatrist friend of mine, I've hewed much closer to the truth and had Breege—in this version a very beautiful girl—enter a convent where she takes the name of Sister Santa Lucia after the patron saint of the blind. Actually Breege today *is* in a convent, just outside Liverpool, only her name isn't Sister Lucia, it's Sister Mary Anunciata. Nothing there. Still, I can't help wondering sometimes if, in the small hours of the morning, there in her cell with its lone candlestick, its prayerbook on top of the small plain bedside table, with a moonbeam slat falling across the heavy wooden crucifix above the head of her bed (I know it's a romantic picture but it's very difficult to imagine a nun's bedroom), she doesn't sometimes wake up and stare at the ceiling as *she* too recreates the scene, tries to take back her warning gesture, or wills the two flying objects to pass wide of the mark. I can see her, vaguely troubled, reaching for her Rosary to say a few prayers for herself, or to pray for Poke, or for Jimmy, or even me.

But perhaps she never thinks of the accident at all, perhaps even if those snowballs had never been thrown, we would today all be exactly as we are. There's always *that* possibility, too.